Who p

W

What was tattooed on Damien Thorn's body in
THE OMEN?
●
Who played Norman Bates in PSYCHO?
●
Which film had the slogan
'In Space No One Can Hear You Scream'?
●
Who, or what, was BEN?
●
Who was THE HITCHER?

Also by Shaun Hutson:

SLUGS
SPAWN
EREBUS
BREEDING GROUND
RELICS
DEATHDAY
VICTIMS
ASSASSINS
SHADOWS
NEMESIS
RENEGADES

SHAUN HUTSON

HORROR FILM QUIZ BOOK

SPHERE BOOKS LTD

A Sphere Book

First published in Great Britain in 1991 by
Sphere Books Ltd

A CIP catalogue record for this book is available
from the British Library.

ISBN 0 7474 0792 4

Typeset by Leaper & Gard Limited, Bristol
Printed and bound in Great Britain by
BPCC Hazell Books
Aylesbury, Bucks, England
Member of BPCC Ltd.

Sphere Books
a Division of
Macdonald & Co (Publishers) Ltd
165 Great Dover Street
London SE1 4YA

A member of Maxwell Macmillan Publishing Corporation

This book is dedicated to Ian Austin,
who actually managed to sell me something
when I *didn't* have food poisoning. I hope
this book lasts longer than your appetite.

Acknowledgements

Apart from the authors of four or five film books which helped me jog my memory while working on this book, there don't appear to be too many people to thank this time round (don't worry, you'll probably be in the next novel, whoever you are ...) but I must just say indirect thanks to F. Maurice Speed, Denis Gifford and Ivan Butler. Apart from that I'd like to thank every cinema I've ever been in during my life, every video shop I've ever rented from and every TV programme planner who has dug up and screened one of the films mentioned in this book.

On a more personal level, many thanks, as ever, to my manager, Gary Farrow; and to all at Macdonald/Sphere, especially Barbara Boote for allowing me to run over deadline and not threatening me with physical violence (well, not much anyway ...). Extra special thanks to my sales team who, as usual, charmed, battled and bulldozed their way into shops for me. Thanks, all of you.

To my Mum and Dad for letting me sit up late when I was a kid to watch horror films on TV. Very special thanks to my wife, Belinda, who during the writing of this book, saw a side of me she doesn't usually see. For putting up with that, for putting up with me and for putting up with being asked dozens of questions every night over the dinner table, thanks. In fact, thank you to everyone who phoned me while I was compiling *Horror Film Quiz Book* only to be faced with a barrage of questions which I'd just written.

And, as ever, to all of you who bought the book, you have my gratitude.

Shaun Hutson

Contents

In the Beginning   1

1 The Silents   5

2 The Golden (and not *quite* so Golden)   13
Age of Horror Films 1930–1956
(Plus 'Quote, Unquote' Part 1)

3 Hammer Films (Plus 'Quote, Unquote' Part 2)   41

4 Urban Horror (Plus 'Quote, Unquote' Part 3)   65

5 Everything But the Kitchen Sink ...   111

6 Cast Off   151

7 In With a Shout   171

8 Once Upon a Time ...   181

9 Odds and Ends   215

Answers   227

In The Beginning...

I don't know about you, but Trivial Pursuit drives me nuts.

It's not the game so much as some of the people who play it. Now I'm only guessing that most of you reading this will have, at one time or another, been subjected to a game of Trivial Pursuit and, worst of all been subjected to playing with the sort of person who asks you not only the exact *weight* of the USS *Missouri* but the names and addresses of all its crew ... They then clutch the question card and gleefully whine 'Oh, this is *so* easy.' At which point I usually feel like rolling that little card into a funnel and ramming it with great force into a tender part of their anatomy.

Quiz books, too, have a tendency to aim questions not at casual readers but at seasoned afficionados of particular pastimes. I mean, if we *all* wanted to answer twenty questions on Pig Breeding in Sussex in the fifteenth Century, we'd all be on the phone to the BBC begging to be strapped into a leather chair and interrogated by Magnus Magnusson, wouldn't we?

The idea behind *Horror Film Quiz Book* is that it should be a bit of fun. I hope it's informative, too, but it's a book to be 'dipped into' rather than one to be pored over like something from the Open University.

Some of you, those who've read my novels, may be wondering: a) why I've produced/compiled a quiz book anyway; and b) what qualifies me to do so.

Well, the answer to the first part of the query is that it comes as a bit of a break for me. I'm not going to bore you with the details of what it's like to write a novel (although I know from the letters many of you write to me that the process interests you) but, suffice it to say that the research, preparation and emotional input required for some of my more recent books has been considerable (for any critics reading this and chuckling I have a brief message: UP YOURS). So, I thought I needed a change. Other writers cope with the strain of writing a novel in other ways. Some don't produce many books; others break up the flow of novels with books of short stories, for instance. Yours truly has compiled a quiz book.

To answer the second part of the question: what qualifies me to do it?

Simple. I love films. I don't purport to be a film expert, a movie buff or whichever other cliché you care to use. I just love cinema. Christ, I've seen over 10,000 films at the cinema, on video and on TV in the last twenty-odd years and, if you asked me to, I could tell you what a medium long shot, a Chinese angle or a pan was (big deal ...) but it's the *experience* of cinema which I enjoy rather than endless critical dissertations about what a certain director was trying to 'say' in a particular film. I've seen films I loved which I *know* are technically awful and, conversely, I've seen technically brilliant pictures which I've loathed but, in the end, it all comes down to a personal opinion. Critics amuse me in most aspects of 'The Arts' and I find that film critics and book critics are very similar. Most film critics are would-be directors or screenwriters while most literary critics are either failed or would-be authors. And the thing which never ceases to irritate them is that films which they hate, or books which they loathe, become huge hits because the only people who matter in the end are the public. Critics are, almost without exception, a waste of space whose opinions count for nothing and the realization of their own worthlessness is what makes most of them so destructive in their criticisms.

But, enough of this aimless ranting and back to *Horror Film Quiz Book*. You won't find questions in here about who was the lighting cameraman on CITIZEN KANE or who was set designer for THE MAGNIFICENT AMBERSONS. Those questions are for film buffs. The questions you'll find in this book are aimed at both the casual film fan *and* those of you with slightly more than passing interest in moving pictures.

When it was first suggested to me that I do a quiz book the first suggestion was that, as I write what are all-embracingly known as 'horror books', the quiz questions should be about horror *films* and, indeed, you'll find a great deal of them are but there are also questions about films like STRAW DOGS, RAGING BULL, THE WILD BUNCH, TAXI DRIVER and MANHUNTER; films which, to me, are as horrific in their own ways as pictures like DRACULA, FRANKENSTEIN and THE EXORCIST, and the former group have certainly been a bigger influence on my own career than the films people like to call 'horror films'. You'll find this argument cropping up again during the introduction to the section of questions on 'Urban Horror'.

In the meantime, contained beyond this introduction you will find over 1,000 questions, split into different sections, to keep you amused or irritated as the case may be. If you want to dip into the book, then fair enough; if you fancy ploughing your way through every single question, then that's fair enough, too. All I ask is that you enjoy yourself.

You'll find, and I make no apologies for it, that some films have more questions about them than others; you'll also find perhaps that your *own* favourite film of all time does not feature anywhere. If so, sorry about that, but, as I said earlier, it all comes down to personal choice in the end. If you can think of any films which have been left out which you feel *should* have been included, then do write and let me know.

For my own part, I've seen almost all of the films mentioned in the book, many of them numerous times. (Two of the films mentioned later on are CROSS OF IRON and ROLLERBALL which I've seen, to date, no less than 43 times each). But the joy is, with the answers being multiple choice, you don't even have to have seen the film to have a guess at the answer. Like I said, this compilation is a bit of fun, not a bloody instruction manual.

Right, that's enough from me. I'll let you plough on with the first section now. Thanks for putting up with my ramblings for a few pages. Good luck with the questions and, with any luck, I'll see you for the next novel.

By the way, if you see a long-haired yob in jeans, cowboy boots and a leather jacket sitting in a cinema one day, buy me a bag of popcorn, will you? ...

Take care of yourselves,

Shaun Hutson,
25 February 1991

The Silents

Don't worry, this section isn't about the life of Marcel Marceau, it's about the earliest days of films (well, horror films to be more accurate).

The silent version of THE PHANTOM OF THE OPERA still contains one of the most terrifying scenes ever put on celluloid. I mean the unmasking of the Phantom by Mary Philbin. Still more frightening than most of the stuff being turned out these days. So, don't skip this section, every question's worth a guess. Besides, aren't *you* anxious to find out which film-maker the Nazis wanted to help them with their war effort? No? OK, fair enough.

One point for each correct answer.

1 Who or what was HEBA in the 1913 film?

      a. The dog woman

      b. The snake woman

      c. The cat woman

2 Who directed NOSFERATU in 1922?

      a. Carl Dreyer

      b. Fritz Lang

      c. F.W. Murnau

3 Who took legal action against the film?

      a. The British censor

      b. Bram Stoker's widow

      c. The Nazis

4 Who played THE GOLEM in 1914?

      a. Werner Krauss

      b. Paul Wegener

      c. Peter Lorre

5 How many silent versions of DR JEKYLL AND MR HYDE were made?

      a. Four

      b. Ten

      c. Seven

6 Thomas Edison, inventor of the light bulb, was the first man to film one of the horror classics in 1910. Which one?

      a. Dracula

      b. Frankenstein

      c. Dr Jekyll and Mr Hyde

7 Who directed METROPOLIS in 1926?

    a. Fritz Lang

    b. Hal Roach

    c. Carl Dreyer

8 What was THE GOLEM made from?

    a. Plastic

    b. Clay

    c. Wood

9 What or who was kept in THE CABINET OF DR CALIGARI?

    a. A vampire

    b. A sleepwalker

    c. An escaped lunatic

10 Who played THE HUNCHBACK OF NOTRE DAME in 1923?

    a. Lionel Barrymore

    b. Sir Cedric Hardwicke

    c. Lon Chaney Snr.

11 The same actor played a vampire in a 1927 film re-made in 1935 as MARK OF THE VAMPIRE. What was the 1927 film called?

    a. After Dark

    b. London After Midnight

    c. The Madmen of London

12 Lon Chaney Snr. played THE PHANTOM OF THE OPERA but what was the Phantom's name?

    a. Erik

    b. Carl

    c. Gustav

13 One scene of the film was shot in colour. Which character does the phantom play during this scene which depicts a masked ball?

> a. Old Father Time
> b. Justice
> c. Death

14 In THE HANDS OF ORLAC, what was the profession of the central character before his hands are severed?

> a. Painter
> b. Pianist
> c. Writer

15 In THE LUNATICS (1913), what was the horrific 'cure' for insanity to be?

> a. Cutting off a hand
> b. Being flayed alive
> c. Cutting out an eye and slitting the throat

16 In METROPOLIS in 1926, what was the name of the mad scientist who created the robotrix?

> a. Rotwang
> b. Ruger
> c. Riedle

17 Who did the STUDENT OF PRAGUE (1926) make a deal with?

> a. God
> b. The Devil
> c. A witch

18 In THE LOST WORLD (1925), what was the name of the professor who led the expedition?

     a. Hawkins

     b. Challenger

     c. Carnegie

19 Who wrote the story on which THE LORD WORLD was based?

     a. William Wilkie Collins

     b. Daphne du Maurier

     c. Arthur Conan Doyle

20 In which year is METROPOLIS set?

     a. 1990

     b. 2000

     c. 2010

21 An important figure in Germany was impressed by Fritz Lang's film and wanted him to work for the Nazi Party making propaganda films. Who was it?

     a. Hitler

     b. Himmler

     c. Goebbels

22 Which film was confiscated by the Gestapo in 1928 because they wanted to use the technical data contained in it?

     a. First Men in the Moon

     b. Woman in the Moon

     c. A Trip to the Moon

23 In THE CAT AND THE CANARY (1927) who, or what, was 'The Cat'?

        a. An escaped lunatic
        b. A masked killer
        c. A crazed actor

24 In THE 13th CHAIR (1926) how is the killer captured?

        a. By a medium
        b. By his fingerprints
        c. By his footprints

25 The first man to play the Frankenstein monster on screen in 1910 was Charles Ogle. How did he earn his living when not acting?

        a. He was a doctor
        b. He was a weightlifter
        c. He was a wrestler

The Golden
(And Not Quite So Golden)
Age Of Horror Films
1930–1956

Everyone – I don't care whether they've never seen a horror film in their life – has heard of Boris Karloff and Bela Lugosi. This section is mainly concerned with the period when those two men were at the height of their stardom, when Universal Films invented or brought to life (excuse the pun) some of the cinema world's most famous creations like Dracula, Frankenstein, the Mummy and the Wolfman. First they made them legends, then they humiliated them at the hands of Abbott and Costello in a series of comedies (and I use the term loosely) which despatched the old monsters far more effectively than a truckload of wooden stakes, silver bullets or lightning bolts.

But, in their heyday, Karloff, Lugosi and their peers reigned supreme. Most of these films in this section I can remember seeing as a kid. Every Friday night on my local TV station, there used to be a horror film on at about 10.30, and my Friday night treat was to sit up and watch it. I can remember sitting through the delights of FRANK-ENSTEIN, THE MUMMY and hundreds more over the years. I'm sure many of you will have seen these old black and white films on TV at some time or another. At the same time (I'm talking mid-sixties now) magazines like *Famous Monsters of Filmland*, *Mad Monsters* and

Monster Mania were on the news-stands and I can remember reading the stories, looking at the pictures, then hoping the films would be put on TV so I could see them.

I built up a large collection of these magazines (some of them very rare) over the years and was calmly informed by my Mum a year or two ago that she'd 'found some of your old magazines in the loft.' Great, I thought, they're probably worth a bloody fortune. I asked her when I could pick them up. 'Sorry, dear, I threw them out,' she told me.

Pieces of my Mum can now be found scattered over most of Hertfordshire and Buckinghamshire . . .

1 What was the first horror 'talkie' made in 1928?

      a. The Killer

      b. The Terror

      c. The Monster

2 In DRACULA (1932), what was the name of the ship which transported Dracula's coffin to England?

      a. The Victory

      b. The Venus

      c. The Vesta

3 In the same film, who played Dr Van Helsing?

      a. Fredric March

      b. Edward Van Sloan

      c. Irving Pichel

4 Director Tod Browning tried to make Count Dracula's eyes look more hypnotic. How?

      a. By photographing them in colour

      b. By getting Bela Lugosi (who played Dracula) to wear contact lenses

      c. By shining thin beams of light at his star's eyes

5 Which day was the film released on?

      a. Halloween

      b. Valentine's Day

      c. Thanksgiving

6 Which Abbey did Dracula secrete his coffin in?

      a. Westminster Abbey

      b. Carstairs Abbey

      c. Carfax Abbey

7 Which part was Bela Lugosi offered after his success in Dracula?

> a. The Phantom of the Opera
> b. The Frankenstein Monster
> c. The Mummy

8 The part finally went to Boris Karloff, but who played Doctor Frankenstein's hunchbacked assistant?

> a. Dwight Frye
> b. Peter Lorre
> c. Lon Chaney Jnr.

9 Where was Karloff when he was spotted by James Whale, the director of FRANKENSTEIN, and offered the part?

> a. Waiting on tables in a restaurant
> b. In Universal Studios' canteen
> c. Serving in a fast food restaurant

10 In FRANKENSTEIN (1931), how does the monster perish at the end?

> a. Shot
> b. Electrocuted
> c. Burned

11 Bela Lugosi's next big starring part was in a 1932 adaptation of an Edgar Allan Poe story. What was it?

> a. The Tell-Tale Heart
> b. The Pit and the Pendulum
> c. Murders in the Rue Morgue

12 What was the name of the mad scientist he played?

> a. Dr Mirakle
> b. Dr Lausard
> c. Dr Chance

13 Another classic monster made his first appearance in 1932. Which one?

    a. The Creature from the Black Lagoon
    b. The Wolfman
    c. The Mummy

14 Who played DR X in the film of the same name in 1932?

    a. Lionel Barrymore
    b. Lionel Atwill
    c. Lionel Stander

15 Two films, both made in 1932, were banned by the British censor. One was THE ISLAND OF DR MOREAU. What was the other?

    a. Freaks
    b. The Inhuman
    c. Murder by the Clock

16 In THE ISLAND OF DR MOREAU, what did the victims of the doctor's experiments nickname his laboratory?

    a. The House of Death
    b. The House of Pain
    c. The House of Hell

17 Which particular trophies was Count Zaroff most fond of in THE HOUNDS OF ZAROFF (1932)?

    a. Human bodies
    b. Human limbs
    c. Human heads

18 What was the film's alternative title?

    a. Hunting Humans
    b. The Most Dangerous Game
    c. The Hunter

19 Which J.B. Priestley novel formed the basis of THE OLD DARK HOUSE (1932)?

    a. Becalmed
    b. Belated
    c. Benighted

20 How was Lionel Atwill unmasked in THE MYSTERY OF THE WAX MUSEUM?

    a. His false face was shattered by Fay Wray
    b. His mask was pulled off by a child
    c. He tore it off himself to terrify a burglar

21 How did the mad waxwork-maker create such realistic models in the same film?

    a. By covering the models with real skin
    b. By covering real people with wax
    c. By stealing bodies from a morgue and preserving them

22 Which 1933 film was billed as 'The Strangest Story ever conceived by Man'?

    a. The Invisible Man
    b. King Kong
    c. The Devil Doll

23 Who was it, in fact, who *did* conceive the story?

    a. Raymond Chandler
    b. Dashiell Hammett
    c. Edgar Wallace

24 How was THE INVISIBLE MAN finally spotted?

> a. His image showed up on a photo
> b. His footprints were spotted in the snow
> c. Someone smelled the whisky he'd been drinking

25 In THE BRIDE OF FRANKENSTEIN, Dr Pretorius (played by Ernest Thesiger) had already succeeded in creating life but his creations had one particular defect. What was it?

> a. They were cannibals
> b. They were giants
> c. They were minute

26 Who played THE BRIDE OF FRANKENSTEIN? (Be careful, this is a tricky one ...)

> a. Mae Clarke
> b. Valerie Hobson
> c. Elsa Lanchester

27 What was the favourite drink of Dr Pretorius in the same film?

> a. Rum
> b. Gin
> c. Whisky

28 What was the name of the plant in THE WEREWOLF OF LONDON (1935) which was said to bloom only at the full moon and could cure lycanthrophy?

> a. Mariphasa Lupino Lumino
> b. Lupine Orchidius
> c. Lupino Lycanthropus

29 In which 1935 film did Boris Karloff play identical twins?

      a. The Black Secret
      b. The Black Torment
      c. The Black Room

30 How did DRACULA'S DAUGHTER meet her death in the 1936 film?

      a. Knife
      b. Bow and arrow
      c. Spear

31 In THE RETURN OF DR X, who played Dr X?

      a. Lionel Atwill
      b. James Cagney
      c. Humphrey Bogart

32 THE HANDS OF ORLAC was remade in 1935. What was the new title?

      a. Hands of a Strangler
      b. Mad Love
      c. Ten Fingers of Death

33 In THE DEVIL DOLL (1933), which infamous prison had Lionel Barrymore escaped from?

      a. Devil's Island
      b. Alcatraz
      c. Sing-Sing

34 In SON OF FRANKENSTEIN, how did police inspector Lionel Atwill come to have a wooden arm?

a. He'd fallen under a train
b. The limb had been infected by a rusty scalpel
c. The Frankenstein monster had torn it off when he was a child

35 In the same film, Bela Lugosi played the monster's companion, Igor. How had Igor's neck been broken?

a. He'd been hung but survived
b. The monster had broken it accidentally during a fight
c. He'd fallen from a speeding coach

36 How did the monster finally perish?

a. Drowned
b. Fell into a sulphur pit
c. Crushed when the laboratory blew up

37 Who played Quasimodo in the 1939 remake of THE HUNCHBACK OF NOTRE DAME?

a. Boris Karloff
b. Lon Chaney Jnr.
c. Charles Laughton

38 In 1941 there was also a remake of DR JEKYLL AND MR HYDE. Who played the dual role this time?

a. Spencer Tracy
b. Frederick March
c. Raymond Massey

39 1943 brought another remake of another classic, this time starring Claude Rains in the title role. What was the film?

     a. Dracula
     b. The Phantom of the Opera
     c. The Mummy

40 What was the name of the executioner, played by Boris Karloff, in TOWER OF LONDON (1939)?

     a. Mort
     b. Mord
     c. Morgan

41 The same film marked the horror debut of an actor who was later to become one of the leading lights of the genre. Who was he?

     a. Vincent Price
     b. Christopher Lee
     c. Peter Cushing

42 Lon Chaney Jnr. actually screen-tested for the part of THE HUNCHBACK OF NOTRE DAME because his father had played it in 1923. True or False?

43 In THE MUMMY'S HAND, how was the Mummy kept alive?

     a. By drinking embalming fluid
     b. By drinking the juice of Tana Leaves
     c. By drinking blood

44 What was the name of the character played by Lon Chaney Jnr. in MAN MADE MONSTER?

a. Electric Eddie
b. Vic Voltage
c. Dynamo Dan

45 In which country was THE WOLFMAN set?

a. Wales
b. Scotland
c. Ireland

46 In the same film, who played the part of the werewolf who bit Lon Chaney Jnr.?

a. Boris Karloff
b. Bela Lugosi
c. Basil Rathbone

47 How was Lon Chaney finally killed in the same film?

a. Shot with a silver bullet
b. Stabbed with a silver sword
c. Beaten to death with a silver-headed cane

48 In THE GHOST OF FRANKENSTEIN, Lon Chaney Jnr. played the monster but whose brain was he finally given?

a. Bela Lugosi
b. Cedric Hardwicke
c. Lionel Atwill

49 It took a lot of bandages to create THE MUMMY. How many yards did make-up man Jack Pierce use on Lon Chaney in THE MUMMY'S TOMB?

a. 100 yards
b. 250 yards
c. 400 yards

50 Both the Wolfman and the Frankenstein Monster rose again in 1942. What was the name of the film which brought them together?

        a. Battle of the Monsters
        b. Frankenstein Meets the Wolfman
        c. Clash of the Titans

51 How, and by whom, was the monster discovered?

        a. By Boris Karloff, encased in concrete
        b. By Patrick Knowles, preserved in mud
        c. By Lon Chaney, frozen in ice

52 Who played the monster?

        a. Vincent Price
        b. Glenn Strange
        c. Bela Lugosi

53 What was the vampire's name in SON OF DRACULA?

        a. Alucard
        b. Tessla
        c. Yorga

54 Two more Mummy films were made in 1944, both with Lon Chaney in the part of the bandaged monster. What were the titles?

        a. The Mummy's Revenge
        b. The Mummy's Ghost
        c. The Mummy's Shroud
        d. The Mummy's Curse
        e. The Mummy's Attack
        f. The Mummy's Bride

55 In HOUSE OF FRANKENSTEIN what was the name of the travelling carnival where Dracula's skeleton was on display?

> a. Lampini's
> b. Grimaldi's
> c. Luigi's

56 How was the vampire count brought back to life?

> a. Blood dripped onto his bones
> b. The stake was removed from his chest
> c. A vampire bat landed in his coffin

57 Who played him?

> a. Bela Lugosi
> b. Francis Lederer
> c. John Carradine

58 How did the Frankenstein Monster perish *this* time?

> a. In an electrical storm
> b. In a swamp
> c. In a river

59 All the monsters were back in another 'get together' in 1945. Name the film?

> a. House of Fright
> b. House of Horror
> c. House of Dracula

60 Thanks to the mad doctor in the film, Edelmann, what ultimately happened to the Wolfman?

> a. He was decapitated
> b. He was cured
> c. He was killed by his father

61 Which real-life villains did Boris Karloff and Bela Lugosi portray in THE BODYSNATCHER (1945)?

    a. Leopold and Loeb
    b. Sacco and Vanzetti
    c. Burke and Hare

62 What was the name of the asylum which gave its name to a 1946 Karloff film?

    a. Bedlam
    b. Broadmoor
    c. Rampton

63 In RETURN OF THE VAMPIRE, workmen accidentally revive Bela Lugosi by doing what?

    a. Taking a cross from around his neck
    b. Pulling a piece of wood from his heart
    c. Spilling blood on him

64 Who turned lupine in CRY OF THE WEREWOLF?

    a. Bette Davies
    b. Evelyn Ankers
    c. Nina Foch

65 In THE DEVIL BAT, what were the intended victims wearing which caused them to be attacked?

    a. A particular colour shirt
    b. A particular kind of aftershave
    c. A particular kind of ring

66 What was the sequel called?

    a. The Devil Bat Returns
    b. The Devil Bat's Revenge
    c. The Devil Bat's Daughter

67 In THE CORPSE VANISHES, how were victims mesmerised by Bela Lugosi?

> a. By drinking a potion he'd made
> b. By eating a special food
> c. By smelling his orchid

68 In DEAD OF NIGHT, the final story features a mad music hall artist played by Michael Redgrave. What is his act?

> a. A juggler
> b. A magician
> c. A ventriloquist

69 Which film was banned for twelve years by the British censors in 1942 because they thought it gave the wrong impression of blood transfusions?

> a. Blood of the Vampire
> b. The Undying Monster
> c. The Mad Monster

70 Which film, made in 1942 and starring Simone Simon, was re-made in 1984 starring Nastassia Kinski?

> a. Vampire's Kiss
> b. Cat People
> c. The Seventh Victim

71 Which film was called, by its director Val Lewton, 'Jane Eyre in the West Indies'?

> a. White Zombie
> b. Zombies of Mora Tau
> c. I Walked with a Zombie

72 What was the title of the short story on which THE THING (1951) was based?

      a. Friend or Foe?

      b. Who Goes There?

      c. Snowblind

73 There was a very famous line of dialogue which ended the film, what was it?

      a. 'They're coming. You're next.'

      b. 'Beauty killed the Beast.'

      c. 'Keep watching the skies!'

74 The Thing itself was actually played by a man who went on to become better known for his roles as a cowboy. Who was he?

      a. Clint Eastwood

      b. Lee Van Cleef

      c. James Arness

75 What finally killed off the Martian invaders in WAR OF THE WORLDS (1953)?

      a. Bubonic plague

      b. Bacteria in the air

      c. An atomic bomb

76 IT, THE TERROR FROM BEYOND SPACE (1956) is widely thought to be the forerunner of a classic late '70s horror/science fiction film. What was the later film called?

      a. Blade Runner

      b. Alien

      c. Close Encounters of the Third Kind

77 Which film carried the slogan 'See it with someone brave'?

     a. Quatermass and the Pit
     b. Curse of the Werewolf
     c. The Abominable Snowman

78 Roger Corman, best known for his numerous adaptations of Edgar Allan Poe stories in the '60s, made his directorial debut with which film?

     a. The Day the Earth Stood Still
     b. The Day the World Ended
     c. The Day the Earth Cracked Open

79 A new monster was launched upon an unsuspecting public in a 1954 film. What was it?

     a. The Creature from the Black Lagoon
     b. The Monster of Piedras Blancas
     c. Konga

80 It spawned two sequels. Name them.

     a. The Return of the Creature
     b. The Revenge of the Creature
     c. The Creature Returns
     d. The Creature Must be Destroyed
     e. The Creature Walks Among Us
     f. The Creature is Loose

81 The director of the 3-D version of HOUSE OF WAX (1953) saw the film somewhat differently to his audience. Why?

     a. He had a rare brain disease which only
        allowed him to see black and white
     b. He had one eye
     c. He was short-sighted

82 Giant animals were very popular in '50s horror films, so what was THE MONSTER THAT CHALLENGED THE WORLD?

      a. A giant moth
      b. A giant worm
      c. A giant sea snail

83 IT CAME FROM BENEATH THE SEA in 1956 but, what was it?

      a. A giant lobster
      b. A giant octopus
      c. A giant crab

84 What was THE MONSTER FROM GREEN HELL?

      a. A giant frog
      b. A giant ant
      c. A giant wasp

85 One particular prehistoric creature revived by atomic tests was billed as 'Makes King Kong look like a midget'. What was it?

      a. Varan the Unbelievable
      b. Godzilla
      c. Reptilicus

86 Stockholm was destroyed, on film, in 1962, by which creature?

      a. Konga
      b. Reptilicus
      c. Mothra

87 GORGO flattened which other capital city two years earlier?

a. Tokyo
b. London
c. Dublin

88 In I WAS A TEENAGE WEREWOLF, what caused Michael Landon to turn into a werewolf?

a. The full moon
b. The school bell
c. School dinners

89 Whit Bissell, as a mad scientist, created another teenage monster in 1957. What was it?

a. Teenage Caveman
b. Teenage Vampire
c. Teenage Frankenstein

90 Both the teenage terrors came together in one film a year later. Name it?

a. How to Make a Monster
b. How to Conquer the World
c. Mixed-up Monsters

91 What was the name of the 'gimmick' used in HOUSE ON HAUNTED HILL which enabled a skeleton to fly out of the screen at an audience?

a. Shockorama
b. Ultra-vision
c. Emergo

92 One 1955 film offered free life insurance for anyone who died of fright during it. Name the film?

a. The Tingler
b. Macabre
c. Maniac

93 How were the audience meant to feel the touch of THE TINGLER in the 1957 film?

    a. Certain seats in cinemas were wired up to electrical charges
    b. Some seats were designed so the springs would burst out
    c. Spiders were dropped from the roof of certain cinemas onto the audience

94 In the same film, how did Vincent Price acquire a fully grown tingler?

    a. By killing a convict
    b. From a mute woman
    c. By experimenting on himself

95 Which 1958 film saw Boris Karloff return to a Frankenstein film, this time as the creator?

    a. Frankenstein Conquers the World
    b. Frankenstein 1970
    c. Frankenstein Meets Dracula

96 Who or what was THE FIEND WITHOUT A FACE?

    a. A giant slug
    b. A maniac killer
    c. An alien brain

97 How did the TROLLENBERG TERROR dispose of its victims?

    a. Disembowelled them
    b. Tore their heads off
    c. Sprayed them with acid

98 In BLOOD OF THE VAMPIRE, how did Sir Donald Wolfitt meet his death?

a. Torn apart by the hospital inmates he experimented on
b. Stabbed by a murderer he was trying to impersonate
c. Eaten by his own guard dogs

99 How was THE FLY killed in the 1958 film? (Be careful . . .)

a. In a spider's web
b. Crushed in a hydraulic press
c. Stepped on by his wife

100 Name the two sequels?

a. Revenge of the Fly
b. Return of the Fly
c. Curse of the Fly
d. Horror of the Fly
e. Son of the Fly
f. There's a Fly in My Soup

'Quote, Unquote' (Part 1)

1 'A toast. To a son of the House of Frankenstein'.
      a. Bride of Frankenstein
      b. Frankenstein
      c. Ghost of Frankenstein

2 'It's interesting to think that 500 years ago, you and I would have been burned at the stake as witches.'
      a. The Wolfman
      b. The Bride of Frankenstein
      c. The Devil Doll

3 'Children of the night. What music they make.'
      a. The Werewolf of London
      b. Dr Jekyll and Mr Hyde
      c. Dracula

4 'Think of it. A brain, waiting to live again in a body I made myself.'
      a. Bride of Frankenstein
      b. Frankenstein
      c. Son of Frankenstein

5 'Even a man who is pure at heart and says his prayers at night may become a wolf when the wolfsbane blooms and the moon is full and bright.'

a. The Wolfman
b. Frankenstein Meets the Wolfman
c. The House of Dracula

6 *'Hurrah for the next to die.'*
a. Dracula's Daughter
b. Son of Dracula
c. Dracula

7 *'What good is a brain without eyes?'*
a. The House of Frankenstein
b. The Ghost of Frankenstein
c. The Curse of Frankenstein

8 *'It wasn't the planes. It was beauty. Beauty killed the beast.'*
a. Son of Kong
b. King Kong
c. King Kong Escapes

9 *'It went for a little walk.'*
a. The Phantom of the Opera
b. The Creature from the Black Lagoon
c. The Mummy

10 *'To die. To be really dead. That must be glorious.'*
a. Return of the Vampire
b. Return of Dracula
c. Dracula

11 *'You have a civil tongue in your head. I know, I sewed it there.'*
a. I Was a Teenage Frankenstein
b. Frankenstein 1970
c. Frankenstein Conquers the World

12 *'I took a gorilla and, working with infinite care, I made my first man.'*
> a. Island of Terror
> b. Frankenstein
> c. The Island of Dr Moreau

13 *'We'll start with a few murders. Big men. Little men. Just to show we make no distinction.'*
> a. The Most Dangerous Game
> b. The Invisible Man
> c. Murders in the Rue Morgue

14 *'For you my friend, they are the angels of Death.'*
> a. Phantom of the Opera
> b. Night of the Demon
> c. White Zombie

15 *'Not to spill blood. That is the law? Are we not men?'*
> a. Island of Terror
> b. The Island of Dr Moreau
> c. Lord of the Flies

16 *'Good and evil are so close they are chained together in the soul.'*
> a. The Wolfman
> b. Frankenstein
> c. Dr Jekyll and Mr Hyde

17 *'She was beautiful when she died, a hundred years ago.'*
> a. Countess Dracula
> b. Dracula's Daughter
> c. Brides of Dracula

18 *'They cut off my head, but Gogol put it back.'*

        a. The Hands of Orlac
        b. Grip of the Strangler
        c. Mad Love

19 *'I offer you immortality. Think of it, my child. In a thousand years you shall be as lovely as you are now.'*

        a. Mystery of the Wax Museum
        b. House of Wax
        c. Terror in the Wax Museum

20 *'Make him well, Frankenstein. Your father made him and he was your father too.'*

        a. Son of Frankenstein
        b. Frankenstein 1970
        c. Frankenstein meets Dracula

21 *'If the house is filled with dread, place the beds at head to head.'*

        a. The Old Dark House
        b. Son of Frankenstein
        c. The Haunting

22 *'There's enough formic acid in his body to kill fifty men.'*

        a. Empire of the Ants
        b. Phase IV
        c. Them

23 *'To a new world of Gods and Monsters.'*

        a. The Old Dark House
        b. The Bride of Frankenstein
        c. Dracula

24 *'An intellectual carrot. The mind boggles.'*

      a. Attack of the Killer Tomatoes

      b. How to Make a Monster

      c. The Thing

25 *'You're in danger. They're already here. You're next.'*

      a. War of the Worlds

      b. Invasion of the Body Snatchers

      c. Earth Versus the Flying Saucers

26 *'Even the moon is scared of me.'*

      a. The Invisible Man

      b. The Wolfman

      c. The Mummy

27 *'They cut out his tongue so the ears of the Gods would not be assailed by his unholy cries.'*

      a. The Mummy

      b. The Mummy's Hand

      c. The Mummy's Foot

28 *'He's all eaten away.'*

      a. The Phantom of the Opera

      b. House of Wax

      c. The Invisible Man

29 *'Your monstrous ugliness creates monstrous hate. I can use your hate.'*

      a. Return of the Vampire

      b. The Raven

      c. The Black Cat

30 *'We Belong Dead.'*

      a. I Walked with a Zombie

      b. Night of the Demon

      c. Bride of Frankenstein

Hammer Films

Hammer films had something which very few horror films have these days, and that was style. They also had, in Christopher Lee, the definitive Dracula and, in Peter Cushing, the best ever Baron Frankenstein. As I had done with the old Universal films, I sampled the delights of Hammer films late on Friday nights but the Hammer films packed a wallop which Universal always missed and an added ingredient which was never seen in the older films. That particular ingredient was blood. However, as a kid of eleven and twelve I was still watching their brilliant productions in black and white (for the simple reason that we didn't have a colour TV). It wasn't until I sneaked into THE SATANIC RITES OF DRACULA back in 1973 (three years younger than the then 'X' certificate permitted) that I first saw a Hammer Dracula film in all its gory glory. I've since been fortunate enough to collect all the Frankenstein and Dracula series on video and can still say that they look as stylish now as the first time I saw them.

Hammer brought class to horror, a class now sadly lacking again with a few notable exceptions. One of their films, CAPTAIN CLEGG, was responsible for giving me my first and only nightmare back in 1963 (thanks, fellas ...). When I first started scribbling little stories at school, they were thinly disguised rip-offs of Hammer Dracula and Frankenstein stories which the teacher would read out periodically. I even wrote a Dracula story as part of an English exam (and still passed). Hammer were a massive influence on my formative years, if not on my career, and I love them for that, if nothing else. In their time, the studio won the Queen's Award for Industry. That same year they introduced Raquel Welch to the world complete with fur bikini in ONE MILLION YEARS B.C. For that alone, surely they deserve a word of thanks . . .

1 In THE QUATERMASS EXPERIMENT, when the rocket returns to earth only one survivor remains. How many were originally in the crew?

> a. Six
> b. Four
> c. Three

2 The infected spaceman in the same film has the ability to absorb living organisms. What kind of lifeform does he first demonstrate this ability on?

> a. A dog
> b. A cactus
> c. A cat

3 How was X – THE UNKNOWN released from its subterranean lair?

> a. Earth tremors
> b. Mine workings
> c. Drilling for oil

4 What did it feed on?

> a. Human flesh
> b. Radioactive material
> c. Oxygen

5 In America, this 1957 film was released as THE ENEMY FROM SPACE. What was its British title?

> a. The Creeping Unknown
> b. Twenty Million Miles to Earth
> c. Quatermass II

6 In the same film, why had the aliens infiltrated an industrial research plant?

a. To create a race of robots
b. To transform the locals into mindless slaves
c. To alter the earth's atmosphere

7 Both THE QUATERMASS EXPERIMENT and QUATERMASS II were based on TV series written by Nigel Kneale, so in 1957 Hammer used another TV play of his called THE CREATURE as the basis of a film with Peter Cushing. What was the film?

a. Curse of Frankenstein
b. Captain Clegg
c. The Abominable Snowman

8 In CURSE OF FRANKENSTEIN, what had been the profession of the man whose hands Peter Cushing acquired for his creation?

a. Pianist
b. Doctor
c. Artist

9 He used the brain of his old teacher in the creature but how did he murder the man to acquire it?

a. Allowed him to die of a heart attack
b. Pushed him down a flight of stairs
c. Pushed him from a coach

10 In the 1931 version of FRANKENSTEIN, the monster was psychopathic because the brain of a criminal was put into its skull. What caused Peter Cushing's creation to become murderous?

a. Its brain was dropped and damaged by
glass fragments
b. Its brain was left out of preserving fluid for
too long
c. Its brain was infected with a disease when
he transplanted it

11 When Hammer remade DRACULA in 1958, the
American title, once again, was changed. Changed to
what?

a. Dracula Returns
b. Horror of Dracula
c. The Mark of Dracula

12 In DRACULA, who played the part of Jonathan
Harker?

a. Michael Gough
b. Phillip Latham
c. John Van Eyssen

13 Peter Cushing, as Dr Van Helsing, was, at one point,
seen using an early prototype of a now familiar machine
(the film being set in Victorian times). What was it?

a. A camera
b. A tape recorder
c. A lie detector

14 Who was executed in Peter Cushing's place at the
opening of REVENGE OF FRANKENSTEIN?

a. A drugged warder
b. A paid helper
c. A priest

15 Michael Gwynn, Frankenstein's creation in the same film, acquired a taste for something after a fight damaged his brain. What was it?

      a. Human blood
      b. Human flesh
      c. Human brains

16 Who played THE MUMMY in 1959?

      a. Christopher Lee
      b. Oliver Reed
      c. James Fox

17 Where, and how, did he meet his end in the same film?

      a. Set on fire in a sewer
      b. Shot to pieces in a swamp
      c. Blown up in a disused mine

18 How did Anton Diffring persuade Christopher Lee to perform the life-saving operation on him in THE MAN WHO COULD CHEAT DEATH?

      a. Threatening to kill his father
      b. Threatening to kill his son
      c. Threatening to kill his fiancée

19 The film was a remake of a 1945 film. What was the earlier film called?

      a. The Man in Half Moon Street
      b. The Mad Doctor of Market Street
      c. Mean Streets

20 Hammer made a film in 1960 about the murderous Thugee cult in India. Set in 1826, it was made in black and white. What was it called?

a. Ganges Ghouls
b. Stranglers of Bombay
c. The Brotherhood

21 Who played Dr Jekyll and Mr Hyde in the 1960 re-make, THE TWO FACES OF DR JEKYLL?

a. Paul Massie
b. Raymond Massey
c. Charles Laughton

22 Dracula himself did not appear in BRIDES OF DRACULA but what was the name of his vampiric disciple?

a. Count Karnstein
b. Doctor Ravna
c. Baron Meinster

23 How did Peter Cushing prevent himself becoming a vampire after having been bitten in the same film?

a. He cut the wound to cleanse it
b. Burned it to cauterize it
c. Boiled it to disinfect it

24 What happened when young Leon (a werewolf) was baptised in CURSE OF THE WEREWOLF?

a. There was an eclipse
b. The priest had a heart attack
c. The font boiled

25 In which country was the film set?

a. France
b. Germany
c. Spain

26 NIGHT CREATURES (also known as CAPTAIN CLEGG) went out in a double bill in 1962 as support to another remake. What was the remake?

      a. One Million Years B.C.
      b. The Phantom of the Opera
      c. Dracula's Daughter

27 NIGHT CREATURES itself featured a group of smugglers who roamed Romney marshes dressed as skeletons to frighten away intruders. In the film, what did the local villagers call these apparently supernatural beings?

      a. The Marsh Monsters
      b. The Marsh Demons
      c. The Marsh Phantoms

28 At the opening of KISS OF THE VAMPIRE, Clifford Evans is forced to destroy his own daughter who has become a vampire. How does he do it?

      a. Decapitates her
      b. Drives a shovel through her
      c. Impales her on a sword

29 In THE EVIL OF FRANKENSTEIN, Peter Woodthorpe played a hypnotist hired by Peter Cushing to help him revive his creature. What was the hypnotist's name?

      a. Zoltan
      b. Zucco
      c. Zebede

30 How did he finally meet his end?

      a. Eyes gouged out
      b. Strangled and hurled over a cliff
      c. Impaled on a metal spike

31 How did Christopher Lee finally destroy THE GORGON?

      a. Forced it to look at its own reflection
      b. Drowned it in the blood of its victims
      c. Decapitated it

32 FANATIC featured a then little-known actor in the part of a retarded gardener. He later went on to international stardom. Who was he?

      a. Donald Sutherland
      b. Percy Thrower
      c. Sean Connery

33 How was Dracula destroyed in DRACULA, PRINCE OF DARKNESS?

      a. By sunlight
      b. By running water
      c. By a bolt of lightning

34 In the same film, Thorley Walters played a mad henchman of Dracula's with a penchant for eating flies. Name the character.

      a. Ludwig
      b. Renfield
      c. Igor

35 What was the support film (also Hammer-made) for DRACULA, PRINCE OF DARKNESS?

      a. Cash on Demand
      b. The Reptile
      c. Plague of the Zombies

36 In the most memorable scene of the film, Brook Williams is menaced by zombies, including his dead wife. How is she killed by Andre Morrell?

      a. Decapitated with a spade
      b. Has her throat cut with an open razor
      c. Has her head split in two with an axe

37 In 1966, Jacqueline Pearce played the victim of a strange curse which periodically transformed her into a vile creature that gave the film its title. What was it?

      a. The She-Monster
      b. She-Devil
      c. The Reptile

38 Which real-life character did Christopher Lee play in a 1966 Hammer film?

      a. Dr Crippen
      b. Rasputin
      c. Svengali

39 In FRANKENSTEIN CREATED WOMAN, what fate befell Susan Denberg's boyfriend?

      a. He was executed for a crime he didn't commit
      b. He was murdered when mistaken for another man
      c. He was accidentally shot by the police

40 In the film, what was her reaction to his death?

      a. She locked herself in a room
      b. She committed suicide
      c. She had herself committed to an asylum

41 Frankenstein rebuilds her into a rather more shapely form but this time it isn't a new brain he transplants. What is it?

        a. New breasts
        b. A new soul
        c. A new head

42 In THE MUMMY'S SHROUD, how does a photographer meet his death at the hands of the Mummy?

        a. He's drowned in developing fluid
        b. Burned with acid
        c. Stabbed with his tripod

43 When the Martian spaceship is first discovered in QUATERMASS AND THE PIT, what is it thought to be?

        a. An unexploded bomb
        b. Part of a wrecked tube train
        c. Debris from an unmanned rocket

44 At the end, how does James Donald destroy the huge 'devil' which is threatening to engulf London?

        a. By running a train into it
        b. With a crane
        c. With an aircraft

45 In THE DEVIL RIDES OUT what is the name of the young woman who is to be sacrificed by the High Priest, Mocata?

        a. Lilith
        b. Judith
        c. Tanith

46 How, upon seeing the Devil, does Christopher Lee refer to him?

> a. The Prince of Thieves
> b. The Goat of Mendes
> c. The Lord of Hades

47 THE DEVIL RIDES OUT was based on a novel by Dennis Wheatley. In 1968 Hammer filmed another of his books. What was it?

> a. To the Devil a Daughter
> b. The Haunting of Toby Jugg
> c. The Lost Continent

48 At the beginning of DRACULA HAS RISEN FROM THE GRAVE, a young boy discovers the body of a girl in a church, suspended from the bell rope. How does this discovery affect him?

> a. He goes into a catatonic trance
> b. He goes blind
> c. He is struck dumb

49 Apparently, Christopher Lee would have preferred a different title for the film. What was it?

> a. Dracula Unbound
> b. Dracula Arisen
> c. Dracula Unleashed

50 How or rather why does the vampire count survive being staked halfway through the film?

> a. His would-be destroyer is an atheist and doesn't pray
> b. Darkness falls as the stake is driven into him
> c. The man staked looks like Dracula but isn't really him

51 How does he dispose of the body of his victim, Zena (Barbara Ewing)?

    a. Chops her up and feeds her to wild dogs
    b. Burns her in a furnace
    c. Throws the body into a ravine

52 At the beginning of FRANKENSTEIN MUST BE DESTROYED, Peter Cushing becomes involved in a fight with a burglar. What does he drop during the struggle?

    a. A brain
    b. A head
    c. Two eyes

53 Who played the unfortunate recipient of the latest brain transplant performed by the Baron?

    a. David Prowse
    b. David Warner
    c. Freddie Jones

54 How does he first see his horrible new appearance?

    a. In the surface of a lake
    b. In the polished wood of a table
    c. In the reflective base of a metal bowl

55 In TASTE THE BLOOD OF DRACULA, Peter Sallis experiences a somewhat ironic death at the hands of his two vampire children. What is it?

    a. He is shot with a silver bullet
    b. He has a stake driven through his heart
    c. He is drowned

56 What was the name of the depraved aristocrat, played by Ralph Bates, who had acquired the dried blood of Dracula?

     a. Lord Dempsey
     b. Lord Courtney
     c. Lord Lucan

57 How is the vampire Mircalla Karnstein finally destroyed in THE VAMPIRE LOVERS?

     a. Shot and burned
     b. Strangled and drowned
     c. Staked and beheaded

58 Who played the role of Mircalla?

     a. Ingrid Pitt
     b. Yutte Stensgard
     c. Stephanie Beacham

59 At the opening of SCARS OF DRACULA, the villagers return from apparently destroying Dracula only to find that their wives have all been butchered. How?

     a. By a swarm of bats
     b. By a pack of wolves
     c. By Dracula's henchmen

60 Dracula's servant in the film shared the same name as a servant in one of the earlier Hammer Dracula films. What was it?

     a. Ludwig
     b. Klove
     c. Thomas

61 SCARS OF DRACULA went out in a double-bill with HORROR OF FRANKENSTEIN, but who played the new Baron Frankenstein?

> a. Christopher Neame
> b. Jon Finch
> c. Ralph Bates

62 Essentially a black comedy remake of CURSE OF FRANKENSTEIN, HORROR OF FRANKENSTEIN reworked ideas but not very successfully. One idea it did use was of Frankenstein using the monster to kill a blackmailing mistress. Who played her this time?

> a. Judi Dench
> b. Kate O'Mara
> c. Veronica Carlson

63 How is Mircalla revived in LUST FOR A VAMPIRE?

> a. Animal blood is poured over her skeleton
> b. Her father allowed his own blood to drip onto her
> c. The blood of a peasant girl is poured over her

64 To retain eternal youth COUNTESS DRACULA bathed in the blood of young women. Why did the blood of a prostitute not help her?

> a. The prostitute had a sexually transmitted disease
> b. The blood had to be from a virgin
> c. The prostitute was anaemic

65 Who did Sandor Eles think she was?

> a. Her own daughter
> b. Her own niece
> c. Her own younger sister

66 She returned to old age at a particularly inopportune time. What was happening as she withered?

> a. She was having sex with her fiancé
> b. She was taking communion
> c. She was getting married

67 In HANDS OF THE RIPPER, how does Angharad Rees kill a fake medium, played by Dora Bryan?

> a. Sticks a hat pin through her eye
> b. Pins her to a door with a poker
> c. Cuts her throat with a broken bottle

68 Where does she finally meet her death?

> a. St Paul's Cathedral
> b. The National Gallery
> c. Madame Tussaud's

69 Mircalla Karnstein made her third appearance in TWINS OF EVIL. Who played her this time?

> a. Kate Nelligan
> b. Katya Wyeth
> c. Julie Ege

70 Peter Cushing played Gustav Weil, leader of the puritanical witch hunters The Brotherhood, in the same film. How did he meet his death in that film?

> a. Stabbed with a machete
> b. Impaled on a spear
> c. Hacked to death with an axe

71 What was unique about the mummified hand in BLOOD FROM THE MUMMY'S TOMB?

a. It had no fingernails
b. It still bled after 2,000 years
c. It needed blood transfusions to preserve it

72 The film was based on a story by Bram Stoker, creator of Dracula. What was the story called?

a. The Lair of the White Worm
b. The Judge's House
c. The Jewel of the Seven Stars

73 In DR JEKYLL AND SISTER HYDE, Ralph Bates played Jekyll but who played his female alter ego?

a. Martine Beswick
b. Diana Dors
c. Judi Geeson

74 In the film, Hyde was linked with a real-life Victorian murderer. Who?

a. Sweeney Todd
b. Jack the Ripper
c. Dr Crippen

75 In VAMPIRE CIRCUS, the vampires arrive in the plague-stricken village to avenge the killing of their bloodsucking cousin. What is his name?

a. Count Karnstein
b. Count Spengler
c. Count Mitterhouse

76 The film was unusual in as much as it used real-life bats instead of special-effects-created creatures. True or False? (Go on, you've got a 50 per cent chance of getting it right ...)

77 In DRACULA A.D. 1972, in the ruins of which church was Dracula revived?

   a. St Augustine's
   b. St Joseph's
   c. St Bartol's

78 The prologue saw Dracula and Van Helsing battling on a horse drawn coach. How does Van Helsing destroy the Count at the climax of that scene?

   a. Pushes him beneath the wheels of the coach
   b. Impales him on a broken coach wheel
   c. Strangles him with a whip

79 The follow-up, THE SATANIC RITES OF DRACULA, originally had a different title. What was it?

   a. Fangs for the Memory
   b. Dracula invades Chelsea
   c. Dracula is Dead and Well and Living in London

80 How many people are photographed, and actually seen in the prints, by the British agent watching the mysterious Pelham House, scene of the Black Mass rituals?

   a. Five
   b. Three
   c. Twelve

81 What does Dracula call the men infected with bubonic plague whom he tries to unleash upon the world?

   a. The Four Destroyers of Man
   b. The Four Takers of Life
   c. The Four Horsemen of his Apocalypse

82 In which fictional town (often used by Hammer films) is the asylum where Peter Cushing is incarcerated in FRANKENSTEIN AND THE MONSTER FROM HELL?

  a. Ingolstadt
  b. Carlsbad
  c. Vaseria

83 What finally happens to the creature he creates?

  a. It is torn apart by the lunatics in the asylum
  b. It cannot bear its own appearance and kills itself
  c. It escapes and falls under a train

84 Who played CAPTAIN KRONOS: VAMPIRE HUNTER?

  a. Derek Jacobi
  b. Rutger Hauer
  c. Horst Janson

85 The script was written by Brian Clemens. Which highly successful TV series had he created in the early '60s?

  a. Thunderbirds
  b. The Champions
  c. The Avengers

'Quote, Unquote' (Part 2)

All the following quotes are from Hammer films. At the moment we're still doing it the easy way. You get a choice of films to pick from. Just wait until the next section ...

Once more, a point for every correctly identified quote.

1 *'Now my revenge is complete.'*

        a. Dracula Has Risen From the Grave

        b. Kiss of the Vampire

        c. Lust for a Vampire

2 *'You will be the four horsemen of my Apocalypse.'*

        a. The Devil Rides Out

        b. Rasputin, the Mad Monk

        c. The Satanic Rites of Dracula

3 *'Frankenstein, I thought the world had seen the last of you.'*

        a. Frankenstein Created Woman

        b. Frankenstein Must Be Destroyed

        c. The Evil of Frankenstein

4 *'Come and see what the mirror of fate will show you.'*

a. Countess Dracula
b. Fear in the Night
c. Vampire Circus

5 '*To skin a cat, first catch it. To tear the wings from a bat, first have it in your hand.*'

    a. Brides of Dracula
    b. Dracula, Prince of Darkness
    c. Twins of Evil

6 '*I say that it is fitting work for any man. Let's all go up there to the castle and put stakes through all their evil hearts, once and for all.*'

    a. Kiss of the Vampire
    b. Taste the Blood of Dracula
    c. Lust for a Vampire

7 '*I am Be, younger son of Rameses the eighth, Pharaoh of all Pharaohs.*'

    a. The Mummy
    b. Curse of the Mummy's Tomb
    c. The Mummy's Shroud

8 '*For your sake, and to protect Elizabeth, I've kept silent so far. But now I'm going to the authorities. That creature must be destroyed.*'

    a. The Gorgon
    b. The Reptile
    c. Curse of Frankenstein

9 '*God would never bless someone so steeped in sin with such a gift.*'

    a. Fanatic
    b. Rasputin, the Mad Monk
    c. Crescendo

10 *'Cut it. Cut deep. Let the poison out.'*

      a. Dracula

      b. Curse of the Werewolf

      c. The Reptile

11 *'Professor, we have no reason to suppose any such creature ever existed in the flesh.'*

      a. The Mummy

      b. The Gorgon

      c. Plague of the Zombies

12 *'The arm is no use to you. I'll remove it this afternoon.'*

      a. Frankenstein and the Monster from Hell

      b. Horror of Frankenstein

      c. Revenge of Frankenstein

13 *'I dreamt I saw the dead arise. All the graves in the churchyard opened up and the dead came out.'*

      a. Brides of Dracula

      b. Plague of the Zombies

      c. Captain Kronos, Vampire Hunter

14 *'I thought you knew. She only takes her pleasure with the Devil.'*

      a. Countess Dracula

      b. Frankenstein Created Woman

      c. The Devil Rides Out

15 *'We were mistaken. The Devil has won.'*

      a. Dracula Has Risen from the Grave

      b. Scars of Dracula

      c. To the Devil a Daughter

Urban Horror

How the hell do you define horror? Before you all go rushing off for a dictionary, I'll save you the trip:

Horror n. 1. Extreme fear, terror, dread. 2. Intense loathing, hatred. 3. (Often) a thing or person causing fear, loathing, etc.

See, covers a multitude of sins, doesn't it? The term horror when used to describe a film or book usually conjures up images of vampires, werewolves, the living dead, etc. Something supernatural, if you like. But that blanket term, I must admit, I find infuriating. Don't get me wrong, I love being called a horror writer (it's better than *some* of the things I've been called ...) but the sort of horror which I write and which applies to this section to come is not the horror of vampires, werewolves and horrible apparitions. It is the horror of physical and emotional violence, of pain, of rejection, of loss, of hopelessness. Films like RAGING BULL portray true horror, the horror of jealousy, of violence, of self-doubt. MANHUNTER shows the horror of a man cursed (or blessed, depending on your point of view) with the ability to think like a psychopath. THE OFFENCE shows the horror of a policeman forced to admit to himself that he finds his own thoughts and those of a child murderer are very similar. The list is endless. You'll find westerns in here (chickens having their heads shot off is pretty horrific, I think you'll agree, especially if you're one of the chickens being shot at), war films (what's worse or more horrifying than war?), vengeful women as in FATAL ATTRACTION and the horror of rape as in THE ACCUSED. Need I go on? The kind of horror in this section is even more frightening because it is more accessible. More of us are likely to experience the horrors of a bereavement or a relationship break-up than we are of walking into a zombie (well, unless we're *very* unlucky ...) Even a film, or films, like THE GODFATHER not only show the horror of violence, they carry an extra feeling of horror when we realise that the wonderful and sympathetic family we're being asked to take a liking to are actually criminals.

Still, *I* liked them. But then, that's the kind of guy I am.

One point for every correct answer, again.

1 What was the name of the maniac killer in DIRTY HARRY?

    a. Gemini

    b. Scorpio

    c. Tarot

2 In Sam Peckinpah's PAT GARRETT AND BILLY THE KID, who hired Garrett to hunt down his former friend? (Character's name please . . .)

    a. Governor Wallace

    b. Henry Hill

    c. John Chisum

3 In the same film, what are Billy and his friends doing in the controversial opening scene?

    a. Shooting at chickens buried in sand

    b. Watching a cock-fight

    c. Shooting at cats and dogs about to be transported by a cook

4 How did the doctors try to cure the plague in THE DEVILS?

    a. With fire

    b. With wasp stings

    c. With snake bite

5 Who played the part of SERPICO?

    a. Robert De Niro

    b. Clint Eastwood

    c. Al Pacino

6 In the 1973 film, how did DILLINGER escape from prison?

a. By taking the Governor's wife hostage
b. Using a gun made of soap
c. Threatening a guard with a razor blade

7 Who played DILLINGER in the same film?

a. Peter Fonda
b. Warren Oates
c. Ben Johnson

8 In CHINATOWN, John Huston insisted, much to Jack Nicholson's distaste, that fish should be served a particular way. How?

a. Raw
b. With the eyes on the side of the plate
c. With the head still on

9 Which famous film star did Robert Blake remind people he was the same height as in ELECTRA GLIDE IN BLUE?

a. John Wayne
b. Alan Ladd
c. Audie Murphy

10 What kind of apparatus did THUNDERBOLT AND LIGHTFOOT use to breach a bank vault?

a. A 25mm cannon
b. A rocket launcher
c. A tank

11 Name the race of immortal beings in ZARDOZ.

a. The Undying
b. The Eternals
c. The Elders

12 How did THE GODFATHER, played by Marlon Brando, meet his death?

> a. He was shot
> b. He had a stroke
> c. He had a heart attack

13 Name the four children of THE GODFATHER *and* the actors who played them. (No help on this one, you're on your own ...)

14 In GODFATHER II, what finally persuaded Al Pacino to seek a divorce from his wife, Diane Keaton?

> a. She threatened to expose him to the police
> b. She had an abortion
> c. She had an affair with his brother

15 What was the name of the powerful Jewish businessman whom the Corleone family formed an alliance with?

> a. Meyer Lansky
> b. Louie Buchalter
> c. Hyman Roth

16 In GODFATHER II, who played the young Vito Corleone?

> a. Robert De Niro
> b. James Caan
> c. Sean Penn

17 IN PRIME CUT, cattle boss Gene Hackman had killed the previous hitmen sent after him but what else had he done to them?

a. Dismembered them
b. Turned them into sausages
c. Fed them to his dog

18 In SOUTHERN COMFORT, what did the National Guardsmen steal which first antagonized the Cajun hunters?

a. Food
b. Weapons
c. Canoes

19 In THE DIRTY DOZEN, why had John Cassavettes been sentenced to hang?

a. He'd killed his commanding officer
b. He'd been involved in a bank robbery
c. He'd raped a woman

20 Who played DIRTY MARY, CRAZY LARRY?

a. Jane Fonda and Jeff Bridges
b. Kelly le Brock and Gene Wilder
c. Susan George and Peter Fonda

21 What was the American title of CALL HARRY CROWN?

a. All Guns Blazing
b. 99 and 44/100 Per Cent Dead
c. 100% Dangerous

22 How many hijackers seized control of the train in THE TAKING OF PELHAM 123?

a. Five
b. Eight
c. Four

23 Who was the last to be caught?

      a. Martin Balsam (who had a cold)

      b. Hector Elizondo (who didn't wear a disguise)

      c. Robert Shaw (who wore a wig)

24 What was Charles Bronson's profession in DEATH WISH?

      a. Interior designer

      b. Architect

      c. Hairdresser

25 Who, or what, was THE MEAN MACHINE?

      a. An aging group of mercenaries

      b. An American football team made up of convicts

      c. A gang of ruthless bankrobbers

26 Who led the bomb disposal team in JUGGERNAUT?

      a. Richard Burton

      b. Richard Briers

      c. Richard Harris

27 Jiro Tamiya played the part of a Japanese detective in which 1972 film?

      a. Yellow Dog

      b. The Bushido Blade

      c. Red Sun

28 Why did Mexican landowner Emilio Fernandez order his men to BRING ME THE HEAD OF ALFREDO GARCIA?

      a. Garcia had robbed him

      b. He had made his daughter pregnant

      c. He had shot his son

29 Warren Oates came uncomfortably near to joining Garcia after being attacked by two other men hunting the Mexican's head. What happened to him?

> a. He was shot and left for dead
> b. He was put in a car and rolled over a hill
> c. He was buried alive

30 Who directed the film?

> a. Sam Peckinpah
> b. Don Siegel
> c. Steven Spielberg

31 In THE GETAWAY, who played the husband and wife bank robbers?

> a. Dennis Quaid and Meg Ryan
> b. Steve McQueen and Ali McGraw
> c. Paul Newman and Joanne Woodward

32 In THE YAKUZA, how did Robert Mitchum atone for dishonouring his Japanese friend?

> a. By cutting off his little finger
> b. By cutting off the tip of his tongue
> c. By cutting his chest

33 Who played LEPKE?

> a. Rod Steiger
> b. Tony Curtis
> c. Ben Gazzara

34 It starred Steve McQueen and Paul Newman, cost a fortune to make, took a fortune at the box office and did for tower blocks what FATAL ATTRACTION did for rabbit stew. What was the film? (And if you don't get this you deserve to play Trivial Pursuit for the rest of your life ...)

35 What was the name of the head drug baron in THE FRENCH CONNECTION?

        a. Lautrec
        b. Charnier
        c. Lausard

36 In FRENCH CONNECTION II, which French city did Gene Hackman track him to?

        a. Paris
        b. Nice
        c. Marseille

37 In BADLANDS, which famous film star did Martin Sheen insist he looked like?

        a. Errol Flynn
        b. James Dean
        c. James Cagney

38 In STRAW DOGS, what was the name of the farmhouse where Susan George and Dustin Hoffman were living and which saw the climactic battle?

        a. Wakely
        b. Scotts
        c. Trenchers

39 Which fearsome weapon did Dustin Hoffman use on Del Henney at the end of their flight in the same film?

        a. A spiked mace
        b. A man trap
        c. A chainsaw

40 Who played the village idiot and suspected killer in the same film?

a. David Warner
b. Peter Arne
c. T.P. McKenna

41 For which city did James Caan play in ROLLERBALL?

a. Houston
b. Chicago
c. New York

42 What was the name of the Indian chief who came hunting for Candice Bergen in SOLDIER BLUE?

a. Running Bear
b. Spotted Wolf
c. Wild Eagle

43 Which real-life Red Indian massacre was it based on?

a. Wounded Knee
b. Sand Creek
c. Yucca Flats

44 What was the futuristic TV system in ROLLERBALL called?

a. Multi-Vision
b. Superscreen
c. BSB

45 Who played THE STREETFIGHTER?

a. James Coburn
b. Charles Bronson
c. Sylvester Stallone

46 Which city was the setting for THE KILLER ELITE?

a. New York
b. Los Angeles
c. San Francisco

47 Which film carried the shout-line 'You Have Been Warned'?

        a. The Exorcist
        b. The Omen
        c. Poltergeist

48 Which film had a character, played by Al Pacino, robbing a bank in order to acquire money for his boyfriend to have a sex change operation?

        a. Dog Day Afternoon
        b. Author, Author
        c. Panic in Needle Park

49 How do Marlon Brando and Maria Schneider first meet in LAST TANGO IN PARIS?

        a. In a museum
        b. They are both viewing a vacant flat
        c. At a funeral

50 Who played THE SAILOR WHO FELL FROM GRACE WITH THE SEA?

        a. Kris Kristofferson
        b. Anthony Hopkins
        c. Keith Carradine

51 Who directed TAXI DRIVER?

        a. Francis Coppolla
        b. Brian De Palma
        c. Martin Scorsese

52 In the same film, what was the name of the young prostitute played by Jodie Foster?

        a. Inga
        b. Iris
        c. Janis

53 The soundtrack was written by a man whose music had graced Hitchcock's PSYCHO. Who was he?

     a. Jerry Goldsmith
     b. Bernard Herrmann
     c. Nigel Kennedy

54 Who were MOTHER, JUGS AND SPEED? (Actors' names please . . .)

     a. Paul Newman, Joanne Woodward and Robert Redford
     b. John Travolta, Kirstie Allie and George Segal
     c. Bill Cosby, Raquel Welch and Harvey Keitel

55 How did Laurence Olivier torture Dustin Hoffman in MARATHON MAN?

     a. By drilling his teeth
     b. By cutting his eyelids
     c. By breaking his kneecaps

56 The American Superbowl final was the setting for a film in which a maniac sniper indiscriminately murdered members of the crowd. What was the name of the film?

     a. Targets
     b. Two Minute Warning
     c. Sudden Impact

57 The same sporting event was also to be the object of a terrorist attack in a film starring Robert Shaw and Bruce Dern. What was the film?

     a. Black Sunday
     b. Death in the Afternoon
     c. Ransom

58 In CROSS OF IRON, how did Maximilian Schell blackmail his adjutant into testifying that he was worthy of an Iron Cross?

      a. By threatening to expose his political ideas
      b. By threatening to report his homosexuality
      c. By threatening to have his family arrested

59 Which real-life murderer was featured in the film HELTER SKELTER?

      a. David Berkowitz (Son of Sam)
      b. The Boston Strangler
      c. Charles Manson

60 In NETWORK, Faye Dunaway used unbalanced newscaster Peter Finch to boost ratings. She also used a soothsayer. What was that character's name?

      a. Sybil
      b. Susan
      c. Morgana

61 Peter Finch, in the same film, announced that he was going to do something outrageous. What was it?

      a. Appear naked
      b. Shoot himself
      c. Expose his bosses as crooks

62 Which real-life kidnapping, thinly disguised, formed the basis of ABDUCTION?

      a. The Lindbergh kidnapping
      b. The Mackay kidnapping
      c. The Patty Hearst kidnapping

63 A more factual account of the same case was made in 1989. Who played the title role?

a. Natasha Richardson
b. Miranda Richardson
c. Vanessa Redgrave

64 Who played the terrified car driver in DUEL?
a. Dennis Hopper
b. Dennis Weaver
c. Dennis Norden

65 The character played by Robert De Niro in this film was called Johnny Boy. What was the film?
a. Bang the Drum Slowly
b. Midnite Run
c. Mean Streets

66 The novel was called *Viper 3*. What was the film called on which it was based?
a. Nuclear Countdown
b. Twilight's Last Gleaming
c. Die Hard 2

67 How did Ryan O'Neal demonstrate his skills to some doubting employers in DRIVER?
a. By stealing a police car
b. By wrecking a car while his employers were in it
c. By driving the wrong way down a one-way street

68 Clint Eastwood directed himself in a spoof of the DIRTY HARRY films, playing a washed-up detective assigned to protect a witness from the Mafia. What was the film?

a. The Gauntlet
b. The Rookie
c. Every Which Way But Loose

69 Brad Davies played real-life character Billy Hayes in this horrific film set in a Turkish prison. What was it?
a. Caged Heat
b. Midnight Express
c. Porridge

70 Where did THE WARRIORS have to battle their way back to in Walter Hill's film?
a. The Bronx
b. Queens
c. Coney Island

71 Name the largest and most powerful gang in the film, headed by the assassinated Sirus.
a. The Turnbull A.C.s
b. The Riffs
c. The Orphans

72 QUADROPHENIA was based on a rock album by which band?
a. The Beatles
b. The Who
c. Pink Floyd

73 In APOCALYPSE NOW, name both the characters played by Marlon Brando and Martin Sheen.
a. Colonel Getz and Captain Williams
b. Colonel Wise and Captain Collins
c. Colonel Kurtz and Captain Willard

74 To what classical tune was the helicopter attack on the Vietnamese village carried out?

        a. The Planets

        b. 1812 Overture

        c. Ride of the Valkyries

75 The beginning of the film featured a song by a legendary rock group. Who were they?

        a. The Doors

        b. The Rolling Stones

        c. Frank Zappa and the Mothers of Invention

76 What was the motto of the air cavalry assigned to help Martin Sheen complete the first part of his mission?

        a. On a wing and a prayer

        b. Death from above

        c. Aces high

77 Who played MAD MAX?

        a. Mel Gibson

        b. Sean Connery

        c. Bruce Willis

78 What was so unique about the actors who played the Younger Gang, the James Boys and the Ford Brothers in THE LONG RIDERS?

        a. They all helped write the script

        b. They were all brothers in real life

        c. They all did their own stunts

79 Which film bore the slogan, 'If you're lying, I'll be back'?

        a. The Terminator

        b. The Exterminator

        c. Death Wish 3

80 In RAGING BULL where did Robert De Niro take Cathy Moriarty on their first date?

        a. To an ice rink
        b. To play crazy golf
        c. Bowling

81 Whose life story was the film based on?

        a. Joe Louie
        b. Rocky Marciano
        c. Jake La Motta

82 Which prized possession did De Niro try to sell to raise bail money towards the end of the film?

        a. A championship trophy
        b. A solid gold boxing glove
        c. The heavyweight belt

83 Which terrorist organization was after Bob Hoskins in THE LONG GOOD FRIDAY?

        a. The PLO
        b. The IRA
        c. The IMF

84 In the same film he ended up killing one of his own men in a particularly nasty way. Which weapon did he use?

        a. A corkscrew
        b. A machete
        c. A broken bottle

85 What was the name of King Arthur's evil son in EXCALIBUR?

        a. Mord
        b. Mort
        c. Mordred

86 In ESCAPE FROM NEW YORK, who effectively *ruled* the island prison into which Manhattan had been transformed?

      a. The King of New York
      b. The Prince of New York
      c. The Duke of New York

87 Prisoners due to be incarcerated in the island prison had an option instead of imprisonment. What was it?

      a. Cremation after termination
      b. Castration
      c. Lethal injection

88 Kurt Russell discovered one of his old partners in crime on the island working for the duke. What was the character's name?

      a. The Thinker
      b. Brain
      c. Squeeze

89 Which country and western singer had an acting part in VIOLENT STREETS?

      a. Kenny Rodgers
      b. Johnny Cash
      c. Willie Nelson

90 In the same film, how did James Caan make his living?

      a. Jewel thief
      b. Train robber
      c. Embezzler

91 Where was SCUM set?

     a. A prison
     b. A borstal
     c. An army camp

92 What was the American title of MAD MAX 2?

     a. Return of Mad Max
     b. White Line Warrior
     c. The Road Warrior

93 Arnold Schwarzenegger played the mythical hero Conan twice. Name both films.

     a. Conan the Conqueror
     b. Conan the Barbarian
     c. Conan the Freebooter
     d. Conan the Avenger
     e. Conan the Stamp Collector
     f. Conan the Destroyer

94 What were the androids called that Harrison Ford was hired to hunt down in BLADE RUNNER?

     a. Duplicates
     b. Replicants
     c. Shadows

95 Which novel was it based on?

     a. The Light that Never Was
     b. Children of a Gifted God
     c. Do Androids Dream of Electric Sheep?

96 Which character, played by Sylvester Stallone, did the film FIRST BLOOD introduce? (No help here ...)

97 Who were the convict and policeman forced to team up in 48 HOURS? (Actors' names please)

    a. Tony Curtis and Sidney Poitier
    b. Eddie Murphy and Nick Nolte
    c. Bill Cosby and Sylvester Stallone

98 Who, or what, was BLUE THUNDER?

    a. A helicopter
    b. A superpowerful policeman
    c. An awesomely effective toilet cleaner

99 Who directed the four individual stories in TWILIGHT ZONE: THE MOVIE?

    a. Martin Scorsese
    b. Roger Corman
    c. George Miller
    d. Brian de Palma
    e. Steven Spielberg
    f. Joe Dante
    g. John Frankenheimer
    h. John Landis
    i. Stanley Kubrick
    j. Paul Bartel

100 Who, or what, was THE STAR CHAMBER?

    a. A group of hitmen who killed troublesome politicians
    b. Self-appointed vigilantes
    c. Judges who re-tried cases

101 Name the fourth DIRTY HARRY film.

    a. Magnum Force
    b. Sudden Impact
    c. The Dead Pool

102 This film created a storm of controversy because of its depiction of violent rape and its horrific aftermath. It starred Brenda Vaccaro as the victim who then kills her attackers. What was the film?

> a. Jackson County Jail
> b. Lipstick
> c. Death Weekend

103 What was the name of the character played by Al Pacino in SCARFACE?

> a. Tony Mantega
> b. Tony Constantine
> c. Tony Montana

104 The English version had two minutes cut from a scene in which one of Pacino's colleagues is killed in a particularly horrific way. How?

> a. With garden shears
> b. With a chainsaw
> c. With barbed wire

105 At the end of the film, Pacino's bullet-riddled body is shown floating beneath a globe which bears what inscription?

> a. The World is Yours
> b. Top of the World
> c. King of the World

106 In THE OSTERMAN WEEKEND, Meg Foster uses a particularly lethal weapon in the film's climactic shoot-out. What is it?

> a. A crossbow
> b. A longbow
> c. A spear

107 What is Rutger Hauer's profession in the same film?

    a. Newsreader
    b. Weatherman
    c. TV show host

108 Who was to be the victim of THE HIT?

    a. Terence Stamp
    b. Richard Burton
    c. Bob Hoskins

109 Diane Lane played a rock and roll singer kidnapped by a gang of bikers called the Blasters led by Willem Dafoe, and rescued by ex-boyfriend Michael Pare. What was the film?

    a. The Cotton Club
    b. Streets of Fire
    c. The Wanderers

110 In RED DAWN what name did the small band of freedom fighters adopt for themselves?

    a. Wolverines
    b. Ferrets
    c. Tigers

111 In BLOOD SIMPLE when M. Emmett Walsh shot Dan Hedaya he left something vital behind. What was it?

    a. His gun
    b. His lighter
    c. His handkerchief

112 What was the name of the prostitute played by Kathleen Turner in CRIMES OF PASSION?

a. China White
b. China Blue
c. Bone China

113 Who played the mad evangelist infatuated with her?
a. Anthony Perkins
b. Anthony Quinn
c. Anthony Hopkins

114 Which pop singer starred in MAD MAX: BEYOND THUNDERDOME?
a. Madonna
b. Tina Turner
c. Janet Jackson

115 Which word had been scrawled, in blood, above the bed of Jeff Bridges' murdered wife in JAGGED EDGE?
a. Whore
b. Death
c. Bitch

116 The actress who played his defence lawyer was, a few years later, to become – in the films at any rate – a killer in her own right. Who was she?
a. Jane Fonda
b. Sally Field
c. Glenn Close

117 What did C. Thomas Howell find in his French fries in THE HITCHER?
a. A worm
b. A maggot
c. A finger

118 Which film carried the slogan 'Nine men who came too late and stayed too long'?

      a. The Warriors

      b. The Wild Bunch

      c. The Long Riders

119 Willem Dafoe was a forger being tracked by undercover cops William Peterson and John Pankow and the film included a car chase during which William Peterson drove his vehicle the wrong way along a freeway against traffic. What was the film?

      a. The French Connection

      b. The Seven-Ups

      c. To Live and Die in L.A.

120 Willem Dafoe was on the right side of the law, playing a military policeman in partnership with Gregory Hines, investigating a number of murders of Vietnamese prostitutes in this thriller set during the Vietnam War. What was it?

      a. Hamburger Hill

      b. Saigon

      c. Platoon

121 Eric Roberts and Jon Voight were two passengers on the RUNAWAY TRAIN. Who was the third?

      a. Rebecca de Mornay

      b. Kelly le Brock

      c. Kirstie Alley

122 In SOUTHERN COMFORT, Powers Boothe had joined the Louisiana National Guard, but which branch of the Guard had he been in previously?

a. Dallas
b. Fort Worth
c. Texas

123 Who wrote the soundtrack to the film?

a. Ry Cooder
b. John Cougar Mellencamp
c. ZZ Top

124 Which film sequel carried the slogan 'This time it's war'?

a. Jaws 2
b. Aliens
c. Robocop 2

125 What was the film in which rape victim Farrah Fawcett-Majors imprisoned and tortured her attacker?

a. Lipstick
b. Sunburn
c. Extremities

126 What did Kyle MacLachlan find in a field which set him off investigating the bizarre events in BLUE VELVET?

a. A human ear
b. A human hand
c. A human toe

127 In STAND BY ME, who played the part of the writer, now grown up, telling the story of his childhood?

a. Richard Gere
b. Richard Benjamin
c. Richard Dreyfuss

128 What did an alcoholic Jane Fonda discover in bed with her at the beginning of THE MORNING AFTER?

     a. A severed arm
     b. A dead body
     c. A dead cat

129 How did mercenary leader Mr Joshua, played by Gary Busey, demonstrate his strength in LETHAL WEAPON?

     a. By bending an iron bar
     b. By holding his arm in the flame of a lighter
     c. By eating broken glass

130 In the same film how was Mel Gibson tortured by Joshua?

     a. He had needles stuck in him
     b. He was given electric shocks
     c. He had his fingers broken

131 Who played Al Capone in THE UNTOUCHABLES?

     a. Robert De Niro
     b. Rod Steiger
     c. Jason Robards

132 Who won an Oscar for his performance in the same film?

     a. Kevin Costner
     b. Sean Connery
     c. Andy Garcia

133 Walter Hill's EXTREME PREJUDICE (1988) was a thinly veiled re-make of a 1969 classic film. Which one?

     a. Easy Rider
     b. The Wild Bunch
     c. Bonnie and Clyde

134 What ended up in a cooking pot, courtesy of Glenn Close, in FATAL ATTRACTION?

> a. A pet hamster
> b. A pet budgie
> c. A pet rabbit

135 What was her profession in that film?

> a. Journalist
> b. Publisher's editor
> c. Public relations officer

136 THE WILD BUNCH received two Oscar nominations in 1969. One was for Best Original Screenplay. What was the other?

> a. Best Director
> b. Best Costume Design
> c. Best Music Score

137 What did the Bunch steal for the Mexican despot who hired them?

> a. Guns
> b. Gold
> c. Horses

138 What did Robert Ryan call his motley gang of bounty hunters who were helping him hunt down the Bunch?

> a. Scum
> b. Gutter trash
> c. Street garbage

139 Robert De Niro played a bounty hunter in MIDNITE RUN. What was the nickname of his quarry?

    a. The King
    b. The Prince
    c. The Duke

140 Bruce Willis ended up fighting for his life in a Los Angeles office block in DIE HARD, but why was he in L.A. in the first place?

    a. To visit his sick mother
    b. To visit his wife and children
    c. To get married

141 What were the terrorists in DIE HARD trying to steal?

    a. Gold
    b. Computers
    c. Bearer Bonds

142 In MANHUNTER, William Peterson was coaxed back to police work by a former colleague, but where had he retired to?

    a. Miami Beach
    b. Florida
    c. Orlando

143 In the same film, what was the name of the criminal genius whom he consulted for insight into the mind of the killer he was pursuing?

    a. Dr Todd
    b. Dr Lecter
    c. Dr Hassler

144 In the same film, for which newspaper did journalist Freddie Lounds write?

        a. National Enquirer
        b. National Examiner
        c. National Tattler

145 In DOA, how did Dennis Quaid ensure that Meg Ryan stayed with him?

        a. He handcuffed her to him
        b. He superglued them together
        c. He tied them together with nylon string

146 THE ACCUSED was based on a true story. Who played the rape victim and who played her attorney?

Victim:	Attorney:
a. Jodie Foster	a. Jane Fonda
b. Cathy Moriarty	b. Kelly McGillis
c. Julia Roberts	c. Meryl Streep

147 This film opens in 1964 with the murder of three civil rights activists and the story follows the hunt for their killers by the FBI. What is the film?

        a. The Klansman
        b. Betrayed
        c. Mississippi Burning

148 Who received an Oscar nomination for his part in the same film?

        a. Willem Dafoe
        b. Gene Hackman
        c. C. Fred Ermey

149 In LETHAL WEAPON 2, how did Danny Glover kill the two men sent to his house to murder him?

- a. With a chainsaw
- b. With a power-drill
- c. With a nail gun

150 What term did Sean Penn use to describe the kidnapped Vietnamese girl in CASUALTIES OF WAR?

- a. A little perk of the times
- b. A little portable R and R
- c. A VC bitch funbag

151 Which song (also featured in CHRISTINE) was Eric Bogosian's theme music in TALK RADIO?

- a. Bad to the Bone
- b. Who Made Who
- c. Heartbreak Hotel

152 In the same film, his wife called him under a false name, pretending to be a real caller. What false name did she use?

- a. Caroline
- b. Carol-Anne
- c. Carrie

153 What did the box delivered to Bogosian's studio contain?

- a. A dead rat and a Nazi flag
- b. A time bomb
- c. Newspaper cuttings about Auschwitz

154 Jennifer Jason Leigh played prostitute Tralala in which film?

>   a. Panic in Needle Park
>   b. Miami Blue
>   c. Last Exit to Brooklyn

155 What was the name of the vicious Japanese criminal pursued by Michael Douglas and Andy Garcia in BLACK RAIN?

>   a. Kato
>   b. Sato
>   c. Mako

156 How did Andy Garcia meet his death in the same film?

>   a. Decapitated
>   b. Disembowelled
>   c. Cut in half

157 Who were the male and female leads in SEA OF LOVE?

>   a. Michael Douglas and Kathleen Turner
>   b. Al Pacino and Diane Keaton
>   c. Al Pacino and Ellen Barkin

158 Who directed BORN ON THE FOURTH OF JULY?

>   a. Oliver Stone
>   b. Stanley Kubrick
>   c. Tony Scott

159 A film starring Keifer Sutherland and Lou Diamond Phillips shares its title with a bestselling novel by Shaun Hutson. What is it?

>   a. Assassin
>   b. Young Guns
>   c. Renegades

160 Which former pop stars played THE KRAYS?

      a. Martin and Gary Kemp
      b. The Everley Brothers
      c. Phil Oakey and Phil Collins

161 Name their two victims. (Actors' and characters' names please.)

Actors:	Characters:
a. Tom Bell	a. George Cornell
b. Terence Stamp	b. Harold Shand
c. Robbie Coltrane	c. Jack MacVitie
d. Steven Berkoff	d. Frank Mitchell
e. James Fox	e. Leno LaBianca
f. Edward Woodward	f. Denis Neilsen

162 Who played JOHNNY HANDSOME?

      a. Andy Garcia
      b. Mickey Rourke
      c. Lance Henrickson

163 Why did Anthony Quinn seek REVENGE against Kevin Costner in the film of the same name?

      a. Costner had stolen money from him
      b. He'd taken his wife away
      c. He'd made Quinn's wife pregnant

164 What was Peter Weller's name before he became ROBOCOP?

      a. Morton
      b. Murphy
      c. Manning

165 Which planet did Arnold Schwarzenegger visit in TOTAL RECALL?

      a. Jupiter
      b. Venus
      c. Mars

166 What were the computerized taxis called in the same film?

      a. Handy-cabs
      b. Johnny-cabs
      c. Quicker-cabs

167 In WILD AT HEART, what did Nicholas Cage call 'a symbol of my individuality'?

      a. His snakeskin boots
      b. His car
      c. His jacket

168 A defence lawyer who has been having an affair with a colleague finds himself under suspicion then under arrest when she is murdered. The film starred Harrison Ford. What is it?

      a. The Verdict
      b. Presumed Innocent
      c. Twelve Angry Men

169 What was THE FIRST POWER, as encountered by Lou Diamond Phillips?

      a. Levitation
      b. Eternal Life
      c. Vampirism

170 Who played the unwanted, dangerously disturbed squatter in PACIFIC HEIGHTS?

      a. Michael Keaton
      b. James Woods
      c. Tom Skerrit

171 Which film had Gene Hackman and Anne Archer trying to avoid hitmen whilst trapped on a train?

      a. The Package
      b. Loose Cannons
      c. Narrow Margin

172 Liam Neeson played DARKMAN, but what had he invented which helped him assume a variety of disguises while he sought revenge against those who'd caused his injuries?

      a. Mechanical limbs
      b. Synthetic flesh
      c. Telepathically controlled robots

173 Who directed GOODFELLAS?

      a. Francis Ford Coppolla
      b. Brian de Palma
      c. Martin Scorsese

174 What was the name of the book on which it was based?

      a. The Brotherhood
      b. Wiseguy
      c. My Life in the Mafia

175 In one scene, why did Joe Pesci shoot a young boy during a card game?

        a. He spilled drink on him

        b. He told him to fuck himself

        c. He threatened him with a knife

176 What was MILLER'S CROSSING?

        a. A railway-track meeting-place

        b. A bar

        c. A wood

177 Who was MARKED FOR DEATH?

        a. Charles Bronson

        b. Steven Segal

        c. Val Kilmer

178 Mickey Rourke played a dangerous criminal who escapes from prison with the help of his girlfriend then finds refuge in a quiet suburban house with two colleagues, using the helpless family as hostages. Name the film.

        a. Year of the Dragon

        b. Angel Heart

        c. Desperate Hours

179 Which film starred Jamie Lee Curtis as a rookie cop who becomes the object of a killer's fantasy?

        a. Blue Steel

        b. Perfect

        c. The Rookie

180 In ANOTHER 48 HOURS what is the name of the drug dealer whom Nick Nolte is obsessed with finding?

    a. The Gypsy

    b. The Iceman

    c. The Outlaw

181 Richard Gere plays a crooked cop and Andy Garcia the man who is determined to bring him to justice even if it means the break-up of his marriage and possible death. What was the film?

    a. The Mean Season

    b. Breathless

    c. Internal Affairs

182 Richard Gere also starred in THE COTTON CLUB which was based on a real-life place in Harlem in the '30s. James Remar played the part of a gangster who frequented the club. What was his name?

    a. Dutch Schultz

    b. Dion O'Bannion

    c. Bugsy Siegel

183 In ALL THE PRESIDENT'S MEN, what is the name of Robert Redford's secret contact?

    a. The Runner

    b. Deep Throat

    c. The Insider

184 What favour did undertaker Bonnasera ask of Don Corleone at the opening of THE GODFATHER?

    a. That he should murder the men who raped his daughter

    b. That he should allow him to join the Corleone family

    c. That he should allow his daughter to marry the Don's youngest son

185 Which rock band both contributed to the soundtrack and also appeared briefly in THE DEAD POOL?

    a. AC/DC
    b. Iron Maiden
    c. Guns 'n' Roses

186 In DIE HARD 2, where is Bruce Willis when he becomes involved in more festive violence?

    a. San Francisco
    b. Washington D.C.
    c. New York

187 What is the name of the drug manufactured by Tom Noonan in ROBOCOP 2?

    a. Nuke
    b. Smash
    c. Crack

188 Which film carried the slogan 'He loved the American dream with a vengeance'?

    a. Bugsy
    b. Scarface
    c. Dillinger

189 In BLUE COLLAR, Yaphet Kotto meets a particularly nasty and unusual end while working in a car factory. What is it?

    a. He's crushed beneath a hydraulic press
    b. He's pushed into a car crusher
    c. He's suffocated in the paint spraying room

190 What was the English title of TRUE BELIEVER starring James Woods?

    a. Fighting Justice
    b. The Boost
    c. Cop

191 Woods also starred as a journalist covering a civil war in South America in this 1986 film directed by Oliver Stone. What was the film?

      a. The Year of Living Dangerously
      b. Salvador
      c. Hidden Agenda

192 Apart from Al Pacino, only two other actors have been in all three of the GODFATHER films. Name them? (No clues I'm afraid ...)

193 What have COBRA, LOCK UP and TANGO AND CASH got in common?

      a. They all share the same director
      b. They all spawned sequels
      c. They all starred Sylvester Stallone

194 There was something in Charles Bronson's military records which kept suspicion away from him in DEATH WISH. What was it?

      a. He had been in the medical corps
      b. He'd been a conscientious objector
      c. He'd been invalided out after a very short time

195 What was the sub-title of DEATH WISH 3?

      a. The Clean-up
      b. The Wipe-out
      c. The Shakedown

196 Teresa Russell was a defence lawyer hired to defend cop Burt Reynolds against a charge of murdering a suspect. What was the film called?

> a. Sharkey's Machine
> b. Physical Evidence
> c. Black Widow

197 In BLACK WIDOW, Debra Winger played an undercover FBI agent trying to track down a killer. She played a similar role in a film with Tom Berenger in 1989 set in America's Deep South. What was it?

> a. Mississippi Burning
> b. Crimes of the Heart
> c. Betrayed

198 Who played the wife of murdered Dan Hedaya in BLOOD SIMPLE?

> a. Frances McDormand
> b. Laura Dern
> c. Mare Cunningham

199 What was Michelle Pfeiffer's occupation in TEQUILA SUNRISE?

> a. Hotelier
> b. Waitress
> c. Restaurant owner

200 Which film carried the shout line 'Will Graham has the mind of a psychopath. Thank God he's on the right side of the law'?

> a. Manhunter
> b. Violent Streets
> c. The Keep

'Quote, Unquote' (Part 3)

Right, this is where the fun really starts. Or perhaps the word fun would be more aptly substituted by the term 'mental torture' ... In the previous 'Quote, Unquote' sections you've had a choice of films from which to try and pick out the quote. Not this time. No clues. Just the quotes, but you can score three times as many points (doesn't that make you feel better?).

You score this section in the following way:

One point for identifying the film.
Another point for adding who said it.
A third point if you can tell me who they said it to.

Not too difficult is it?
  Right, off you go.

1 'Let it go. Or I'll give you a war you won't believe.'

2 'Did you know that me and Alan Ladd were exactly the same height?'

3 'When I see a naked man chasing a woman with a butcher knife and a hard-on, I figure he's not collecting for the Red Cross.'

4 'This could be one of the big moments of your life. Don't make it your last.'

5 'Never trust a man whose eyebrows meet in the middle.'

6 'I love the smell of napalm in the morning.'

7 'To hell with the goddam passengers. What do they expect for their lousy fifty cents? To live forever?'

8 'Sticks and stones may break your bones but words do permanent damage.'

9 'I want reliable people. People who aren't going to get carried away. I mean, we're not murderers, in spite of what this undertaker says.'

10 'Sixteen people are dead because of it. Him and him and you and me. And one of them was a damned good friend of mine.'

11 'When you side with a man you stay with him and if you can't do that you're like some animal.'

12 'You're to take good advice. You're not to play in Tokyo, you're not to play again.'

13 'I ain't about to argue with no Apache over horseshit, Lieutenant.'

14 'My little brother was thirteen years old. You think about that. On your way to hell.'

15 'Someone's kidnapped justice and hidden it inside the law.'

16 'If you don't get back we're going to start throwing bodies out of the door one at a time.'

17 'So give me a stage where this bull here can rage and though I can fight I'd much rather recite. That's entertainment.'

18 'I think he feels he's on some kind of special mission. That is to achieve spiritual domination of his battalion. Thereby symbolising the purity of the great German Wermacht itself.'

19 'Now you listen to me you backwoods shithead. If you don't go and fetch the sheriff right now I'm going to kick that door in.'

20 'He's been fighting Villa and losing but, with enough guns, he could become a power in northern Mexico. My guess is Pike will try to get them for him.'

21 'If shit was money, poor people wouldn't have assholes.'

22 'The first thought he was invincible, the second thought he could fly. They were both wrong.'

23 'You ask me what's best for your daughter? Six months, under observation, in the best clinic you can find.'

24 'Blood stains on the west wall indicate arterial spray. Even with his throat cut Leeds tried to fight because he knew the intruder was moving to the children.'

25 'You're the only one left in this family with my father's strength.'

26 'Some day a real rain'll come and wash all the scum off the streets.'

27 'And get that beard cut. You look like an asshole with dentures.'

28 'Definition of a scientist. A man who understood nothing, until there was nothing left to understand.'

29 'After hunting a man, animals just don't rate.'

30 'Conscientious objectors are unlikely vigilantes.'

31 'It's a walk-in bank. A piece of cake. You don't have to be Dillinger for that.'

32 'No Zulu twenty years out of a tree is going to shove fifty cents in my hand and tell me there's a freighter in Johannesburg harbour waiting to take me away from the country I built.'

33 'Harry thinks that if you call him Harry one more time he's gonna' make you eat that cat.'

34 'You're so busy doing the dirty work you can't tell who the bad guys really are.'

35 'People say that if you'd driven the blacks north twenty years ago, we'd have a football stadium here now. But, just like this county's out of step with the rest of the world, you're out of step with the goddam county.'

36 'You don't die for women, you kill for them.'

37 'Do I sound like I'm ordering a fucking pizza?'

38 'This weapon fires 500 rounds of 9mm ammunition per minute which means that if all of you were to simultaneously rush me, not one of you would get any further than you are right now.'

39 'He comes after you with a knife, you go after him with a gun. He puts one of yours in the hospital, you put one of his in the morgue. That's the Chicago way.'

40 'I want a cop who can speak English, knows his way round the streets and can find his ass with two hands.'

41 'When people are afraid of you, you can do anything.'

42 'Garage freak? What kind of crazy fucking story is this?'

43 'Go ahead. Make my day.'

44 'We were like movie stars with muscle.'

45 'I know what you're thinking. Did he fire six shots or only five. Well, to tell you the truth I've kind of forgotten myself in all this excitement. But being as this is a .44 Magnum, the most powerful handgun in the world and I could blow your head clean off, you've got to ask yourself a question. Do I feel lucky?'

46 'You can't polish a turd.'

47 'You cross me and I'll put holes in her you never even thought of.'

48 'I think he looks on me as some kind of kindred spirit.'

49 'The bullshit piled up so fast in Vietnam you needed wings to stay above it.'

50 'There's good news and bad news. The good news is yes, I am a cop and I have to take you in. The bad news is I'm suspended and I don't give a fuck.'

Everything But The Kitchen Sink ...

I was trying to think of a snappy title for this particular section, but then looking over the questions I realized that a snappy, witty, erudite title was out of place. Besides, there is everything but the kitchen sink in here anyway. Questions on old horror films, new horror films, urban horror. Anything, in fact, that came into my mind.

You may find that some of the questions have already appeared in previous sections and there are one or two good reasons for that.

The first reason is that this book was written about ten months before you actually got your hands on it and my publishers needed to see the type of questions which the book was going to contain once it was finished, so yours truly produced 200 questions basically to show them what they were getting. I then went back and did the book in the chronological sections (as previously explained) and found that I was occasionally using some of the questions that I'd originally used experimentally (if you follow me...?) Hence the duplication of some questions you've already seen and answered.

The other reason is I just forgot which questions I'd asked. Trying to compile a book like this is so different, obviously, to writing a novel that things sometimes get (to quote G.D. Spradlin in APOCALYPSE NOW) 'a little confused out there ...' So, apologies if you've already answered some of the questions, but look at it this way, at least if you got them right there's some in this section you know you're going to be correct on. OK, so it's not much of a consolation, but it's the best I could do.

Anyway, on with the questions and, just a word of warning. Although this section is called 'Everything But the Kitchen Sink ...' if a sink does happen to creep in once or twice, then you have been warned. Things are never what they seem.

That's probably a quote from somewhere or other. If you find out what, then let me know.

On with the questions ...

1 Who played Norman Bates in PSYCHO?

      a. John Gavin
      b. Anthony Hopkins
      c. Anthony Perkins

2 What was Boris Karloff's real name?

      a. John Smith
      b. Frederick Bloggs
      c. William Henry Pratt

3 What was the name of the killer in HALLOWEEN?

      a. George
      b. Michael
      c. Frank

4 Who wrote DRACULA (the novel)?

      a. Charles Dickens
      b. Bram Stoker
      c. William Wilkie Collins

5 What was the name of the spaceship in ALIEN?

      a. The Monstro
      b. The Monolith
      c. The Nostromo

6 What was Lon Chaney Snr's nickname?

      a. Man of a thousand faces
      b. Man of a hundred disguises
      c. Man of a million talents

7 Who was THE EXORCIST?

      a. Laurence Olivier
      b. Max Von Sydow
      c. Richard Burton

8 In THE FOG, what was the name of the ghost ship?

a. The Rose

b. The Marie Celeste

c. The Elizabeth Dane

9 Who was THE HITCHER?

a. Rutger Hauer

b. Tom Cruise

c. Dennis Hopper

10 Name the killer in the FRIDAY THE 13TH films? (Well, the first one anyway . . .)

a. Marvin

b. Jason

c. Freddy

11 How many times has Christopher Lee played Dracula?

a. Five times

b. Ten times

c. Eight times

12 What was the profession of the identical twins in DEAD RINGERS?

a. Doctors

b. Gynaecologists

c. Dentists

13 Where did GODZILLA come from?

a. Hong Kong

b. China

c. Japan

14 What did the zombies in RETURN OF THE LIVING DEAD feed on?

      a. Hearts
      b. Kidneys
      c. Brains

15 In THE FLY (the remake), which animal did Jeff Goldblum first experiment on?

      a. Baboon
      b. Cat
      c. Dog

16 His name is Robert Englund but which character is he better known as?

      a. Freddy Kruger
      b. Michael Myers
      c. Jason Vorhees

17 What did William Hurt change into in ALTERED STATES?

      a. A werewolf
      b. A lizard
      c. An ape

18 How did THE ABOMINABLE DOCTOR PHIBES dispose of his victims?

      a. By using toxic waste
      b. By imitating the plagues of Israel
      c. By chainsaw

19 What was the name of the Yorkshire pub visited by the two Americans in AN AMERICAN WEREWOLF IN LONDON?

a. The Hanged Man
b. The Woolpack
c. The Slaughtered Lamb

20 In THE AMITYVILLE HORROR the daughter of the Lutz family had a ghostly playmate. What kind of animal was it?

a. A goat
b. A pig
c. A wolf

21 How many sequels to the film have so far been released?

a. One
b. Two
c. Three

22 Which then unknown actor had a small role in THE BEAST FROM 20,000 FATHOMS in 1953, as the sniper responsible for killing it?

a. Clint Eastwood
b. Yul Bryner
c. Lee Van Cleef

23 Who wrote the short story, 'The Foghorn', on which the film was based?

a. Isaac Asimov
b. Ray Bradbury
c. Arthur C. Clarke

24 Who directed THE BIRDS? (No help on this one ...)

25 What kind of creature was the beast in THE BEAST MUST DIE?

a. Vampire
b. Werewolf
c. Zombie

26 At the prologue to BRIDE OF FRANKENSTEIN (1935), the creator of Frankenstein, Mary Shelley, was portrayed by which actress?

a. Vivien Leigh
b. Olivia de Havilland
c. Elsa Lanchester

27 Which budding actor had his film debut in the 1958 version of THE BLOB?

a. Steve McQueen
b. Paul Newman
c. Robert Redford

28 There was a sequel made in 1973 which, despite being released in Britain as BEWARE THE BLOB, also had an alternative title. What was it?

a. The Return of the Blob
b. Son of Blob
c. Vengeance of the Blob

29 One of the following three characters has *never* appeared as a vampire in a Hammer film. Which character?

a. Baron Meinster
b. Doctor Ravna
c. Count Orlock

30 What was so lethal about the mutant cockroaches in BUG?

a. They could make fire
b. They were indestructible
c. They drank blood

31 What were the creatures in THE BROOD known as?

    a. The children of the damned
    b. The children of Hell
    c. The children of rage

32 How did Oliver Reed meet his death in BURNT OFFERINGS?

    a. Shot
    b. Pushed from a window
    c. Decapitated with cheese wire

33 How was CARRIE humiliated at her school prom?

    a. She had pigs' blood poured over her
    b. She had her dress smeared with
       excrement
    c. She had her hair cut off

34 In THE CAR there was one place where the demonic vehicle could not go. Where was it?

    a. A hospital
    b. A churchyard
    c. A playground

35 Based on M.R. James' story 'Casting the Runes', this film featured a cynical psychic investigator pitted against a black magician who can summon a monstrous being to murder all those whom he manages to pass a piece of ancient paper to. What was the film?

    a. The Legacy
    b. Night of the Demon
    c. The Damned

36 In TO THE DEVIL ... A DAUGHTER who was the actress pregnant with Satan's child?

        a. Jodie Foster
        b. Brooke Shields
        c. Nastassia Kinski

37 Who, or what, was CHRISTINE?

        a. A haunted TV set
        b. A haunted lorry
        c. A haunted car

38 Which river was home to THE CREATURE FROM THE BLACK LAGOON?

        a. The Nile
        b. The Thames
        c. The Amazon

39 In THE CREEPING FLESH, in which country had Peter Cushing discovered the giant skeleton of what he thought was a missing link?

        a. Africa
        b. Borneo
        c. Java

40 In the same film, how was the creature brought back to life?

        a. By drinking blood
        b. By being sprinkled with salt
        c. By being touched with rainwater

41 What was CUJO?

        a. A dog
        b. A cat
        c. A gerbil

42 Which country was CURSE OF THE WEREWOLF set in?

> a. France
> b. Spain
> c. Germany

43 How did the survivors in DAWN OF THE DEAD block the entrances to the huge shopping mall where they were trapped?

> a. By boarding them up
> b. By electrifying them
> c. By putting lorries in front of them

44 What was the creature the Hittites feared in DEADLY BLESSING?

> a. The Banshee
> b. The Siren
> c. The Incubus

45 How did James Franciscus discover that he himself was a member of the living dead in DEAD AND BURIED?

> a. He read it in the paper
> b. He saw a film of his own death
> c. His wife told him

46 How many years had Christopher Walken been in a coma in THE DEAD ZONE?

> a. Ten years
> b. Seven years
> c. Four years

47 Which city is DON'T LOOK NOW set in?

a. Rome
b. Venice
c. Paris

48 In THE EVIL DEAD, what was the only way to destroy those possessed by demons?
    a. Dismemberment
    b. Decapitation
    c. Disembowelling

49 In EVIL DEAD 2, after Bruce Campbell has been forced to cut off his own hand, he covers the offending limb with a bucket and weighs it down with a pile of books. What is the title of the top book on the pile?
    a. Arms and the Man
    b. A Farewell to Arms
    c. Palm-Reading Made Easy

50 What was Norman Bates' hobby in PSYCHO?
    a. Stamp collecting
    b. Bird watching
    c. Taxidermy

51 How did he kill his *real* mother in PSYCHO II?
    a. With poison
    b. With a knife
    c. With a shovel

52 What finally convinced Father Karras (Jason Miller) that Regan (Linda Blair) was possessed in THE EXORCIST?
    a. She spoke a foreign language
    b. He saw the words 'help me' rise on her stomach
    c. She vomited on him

53 In the same film, what was the profession of the possessed girl's mother?

> a. Writer
> b. Actress
> c. TV presenter

54 How many teenagers were trapped in THE FUNHOUSE?

> a. Six
> b. Eight
> c. Four

55 What was the name of the town menaced by THE FOG?

> a. Echo Bay
> b. Antonio Bay
> c. Lookout Bay

56 In the same film, how many people were required to die in order to appease the ghostly lepers?

> a. Four
> b. Five
> c. Six

57 Which cinematic gimmick made FLESH FOR FRANKENSTEIN even more shocking?

> a. Smell-o-vision
> b. Stereo
> c. 3-D

58 BLOOD FOR DRACULA was released at about the same time with Udo Kier switching to the role of Dracula. Why was he ill after sucking the blood of one of his host's daughters?

a. She had a sexually transmitted disease
b. She wasn't a virgin
c. She was anaemic

59 In HALLOWEEN, how old was Michael Myers when he was committed to an asylum?

a. Ten
b. Six
c. Four

60 In HALLOWEEN 2, he continued trying to kill Jamie Lee Curtis. What relation was she to him?

a. Sister
b. Cousin
c. Niece

61 In HALLOWEEN 3: SEASON OF THE WITCH, what was the name of the company which made the lethal masks?

a. Silver Seal
b. Silver Dollar
c. Silver Shamrock

62 Which pop star had a role in THE HUNGER?

a. Alice Cooper
b. Mick Jagger
c. David Bowie

63 What was the name of Robert Shaw's boat in JAWS?

a. The Orca
b. The Rose
c. The Seagrass

64 What was the name of the island where KING KONG lived in the original 1933 version?

        a. Death Island

        b. Devil Island

        c. Skull Island

65 In the remake of KING KONG in 1976, which building did the giant ape climb to the top of?

        a. The Empire State Building

        b. The World Trade Centre

        c. The Occidental Tower

66 THE MANITOU began as a growth on which part of its victim's body?

        a. The back

        b. The neck

        c. The arm

67 Who played THE LAST MAN ON EARTH?

        a. Peter Cushing

        b. Christopher Lee

        c. Vincent Price

68 Which film did Charlton Heston repeatedly watch in THE OMEGA MAN?

        a. The Wild Bunch

        b. Woodstock

        c. Easy Rider

69 Both THE LAST MAN ON EARTH and THE OMEGA MAN were based on the same novel. What was it?

        a. I am Legend

        b. The Totem

        c. Erebus

70 Which number did Damien Thorn have tattooed on his body which marked him out as the Antichrist in THE OMEN? (No help here either . . .)

71 In OMEN 2, how did William Holden finally recognize Damien as the Antichrist?
> a. From a photo
> b. From a painting
> c. From a sculpture

72 In THE FINAL CONFLICT, who finally destroyed Damien Thorn?
> a. Jesus Christ
> b. God
> c. A priest

73 Which famous horror author wrote the short story on which THE PIT AND THE PENDULUM was based?
> a. H.P. Lovecraft
> b. Edgar Allen Poe
> c. Robert E. Howard

74 Which film featured a story about the same author?
> a. Chamber of Horrors
> b. Torture Garden
> c. Asylum

75 What was the name of the London street where the alien spaceship was found in QUATERMASS AND THE PIT?
> a. Cobbs Lane
> b. Jobs Lane
> c. Hobs Lane

76 Which rock star made a short but violent appearance in PRINCE OF DARKNESS?

  a. Alice Cooper
  b. David Lee Roth
  c. W. Axl Rose

77 Which normally jovial character murdered Joan Collins in TALES FROM THE CRYPT?

  a. The Easter Bunny
  b. Porky Pig
  c. Father Christmas

78 How many wishes did THE MONKEY'S PAW give?

  a. Two
  b. Three
  c. Four

79 Ray Milland is so terrified of being buried alive he creates a coffin for himself complete with tools for his escape should his ultimate fear come true. However, despite his contingency plans the unthinkable still happens in THE PREMATURE BURIAL. How is he actually released from his coffin?

  a. By an earth tremor
  b. By rats
  c. By bodysnatchers

80 What was the American title of WITCHFINDER GENERAL?

  a. The Killer Priest
  b. The Conqueror Worm
  c. The Deadly Searcher

81 In the same film, which infamous real-life witch-hunter did Vincent Price portray?

    a. Matthew Hopkins
    b. Torquemada
    c. Cardinal Richelieu

82 In POLTERGEIST, one particular child's toy took on a malevolent life of its own. What was it?

    a. A doll
    b. A stuffed clown
    c. A teddy bear

83 In RABID, where, on her body, was the needle-like device hidden with which Marilyn Chambers infected her victims?

    a. In her mouth
    b. On her hand
    c. Under her arm

84 Who supplied the rock music soundtrack for MAXIMUM OVERDRIVE?

    a. Iron Maiden
    b. AC/DC
    c. Motley Crue

85 What was the name of the amiable parasite in BRAIN DAMAGE?

    a. George
    b. Alvin
    c. Elmer

86 In THEATRE OF BLOOD, Vincent Price murdered his victims by adapting scenes from Shakespeare plays. Which play formed the basis for the first killing, that of Michael Horden by a bunch of down and outs?

a. Julius Ceasar
b. Titus Andronicus
c. Cymbeline

87 What was the name of the hotel of which Jack Nicholson was caretaker in THE SHINING?

a. The Outlook
b. The Overlook
c. The Overview

88 'To Sleep, Perchance to Scream' was the slogan on the posters for which film?

a. Nightmare on Elm Street
b. Dream Demon
c. Night of the Demon

89 Who, or what, were THEM?

a. Spiders
b. Worms
c. Ants

90 According to Warner Oland in WEREWOLF OF LONDON, what does the werewolf always kill?

a. Its mother
b. Its father
c. The thing it loves

91 The infected people in SHIVERS lived in a luxury apartment block. What was it called?

a. Glitter tower
b. Starliner tower
c. Celebrity tower

92 The creature in LAIR OF THE WHITE WORM wasn't in fact a worm. What was it?

        a. A huge maggot
        b. An ancient snake
        c. A prehistoric reptile

93 Who wrote the short story on which the film was based?

        a. Bram Stoker
        b. H.P. Lovecraft
        c. Edgar Allan Poe

94 The same writer wrote a story about an avenging Egyptian mummy which was filmed by Hammer as BLOOD FROM THE MUMMY'S TOMB. What was the short story called?

        a. Jewel of the Nile
        b. Jewel in the Crown
        c. Jewel of the Seven Stars

95 What was John Carradine guarding in THE SENTINEL?

        a. The entrance to Hell
        b. The secret of eternal life
        c. A fortune in gold

96 Which real-life chat show host featured in MADHOUSE?

        a. Jonathan Ross
        b. Michael Aspel
        c. Michael Parkinson

97 What was the name of the island visited by Edward Woodward in THE WICKER MAN?

      a. Fairisle
      b. Summerisle
      c. Demonisle

98 In the same film, the islanders had a rather curious way of curing a sore throat. What was it?

      a. Eating raw meat
      b. Drinking blood
      c. Putting a toad in their mouths

99 In FRANKENSTEIN AND THE MONSTER FROM HELL, what prevented Peter Cushing from performing surgery?

      a. He was blind in one eye
      b. His hands had been burned
      c. His fingers had been broken

100 What kind of antique turned David Warner into a psychopathic murderer in FROM BEYOND THE GRAVE?

      a. A mirror
      b. A statue
      c. A snuff box

101 Who played Dracula in VAMPIRA in 1974?

      a. Christopher Lee
      b. David Niven
      c. Vincent Price

102 Where was the mutant baby finally cornered in IT'S ALIVE?

      a. In a nursery
      b. In a hospital
      c. In a sewer

103 In which city was LEGEND OF THE WEREWOLF set?

      a. London
      b. Paris
      c. Moscow

104 How was Count Mitterhouse finally destroyed in VAMPIRE CIRCUS?

      a. Staked through the heart
      b. Burned
      c. Decapitated

105 What was the name of the chainsaw-wielding killer in THE TEXAS CHAINSAW MASSACRE?

      a. Deathshead
      b. Pus face
      c. Leatherface

106 Who, or what, was ZOLTAN?

      a. Dracula's dog
      b. Dracula's bat
      c. Dracula's servant

107 Where did the terrifying events of TOWER OF EVIL take place?

      a. A castle
      b. A lighthouse
      c. A church

108 How did the army of bloodworms finally get inside the house at the end of SQUIRM?

      a. Under a door
      b. Through a window
      c. Through the shower

109 BLUE SUNSHINE turned its victims into killers. What was it?

        a. Contaminated food

        b. A disease

        c. A drug

110 A girl travels to Germany to attend a music academy and while she's there she's caught up in a series of grisly murders including one of a blind man who's savaged by his own dog. What is the film?

        a. Tenebrae

        b. Suspiria

        c. Inferno

111 In TENEBRAE, the murderer's victims are found with something stuffed in their mouths. What is it?

        a. Newspaper

        b. Pages of the Bible

        c. Pages from a bestselling novel

112 What had the mutant fish in PIRANHA originally been bred for?

        a. Food

        b. As a weapon in the Vietnam War

        c. To clean up rivers

113 What was the name of the leader of the cannibal family in THE HILLS HAVE EYES?

        a. Pluto

        b. Jupiter

        c. Mars

114 In DEATHTRAP, Neville Brand kept a particularly fearsome pet. What was it?

        a. A tiger
        b. A timber wolf
        c. A crocodile

115 What kind of creatures featured in NIGHTWING?

        a. Vampire bats
        b. Killer owls
        c. Eagles

116 What was the name of the summer camp where the murders took place in FRIDAY THE 13TH?

        a. Placid Lake
        b. Crystal Lake
        c. Happy Lake

117 In FRIDAY THE 13TH PART 2, what did Jason keep in his fridge?

        a. The head of his first victim
        b. His mother's head
        c. His beer

118 What kind of weapon was used to kill Angie Dickinson in DRESSED TO KILL?

        a. A knife
        b. A piece of glass
        c. An open razor

119 In SCANNERS, how did Michael Ironside come to have a hole in the centre of his forehead?

        a. He'd been shot there
        b. He'd used a chisel on himself
        c. He'd used a drill on himself

120 In THE THING (1982), how did Kurt Russell prove to his companions that he wasn't controlled by the shape-changing alien?

> a. A blood test
> b. A urine test
> c. A saliva test

121 Name the character, in the film, who had created VIDEODROME?

> a. David Destruction
> b. George Gore
> c. Brian Oblivion

122 What was the chief side-effect of watching VIDEODROME? (In the movie, I mean, not the *real* effects on cinemagoers ...)

> a. It made viewers go insane
> b. It induced blindness
> c. It induced brain tumours

123 Who, or what, were THE LOST BOYS?

> a. Werewolves
> b. Vampires
> c. Zombies

124 In the same film, what was the name of the vampire-hunting duo who ran a comic shop?

> a. The Frog Brothers
> b. The Toad Brothers
> c. The Newt Brothers

125 Who was THE TERMINATOR? (No help on this one ...)

126 In REANIMATOR, what was the first animal that Herbert West brought back to life?

        a. A tortoise
        b. A frog
        c. A cat

127 In FROM BEYOND, what was the name of the mad doctor experimenting with the pineal gland?

        a. Pretorius
        b. Gregor
        c. Vanderburg

128 Who played Lucifer in ANGEL HEART?

        a. Rod Steiger
        b. Robert De Niro
        c. Al Pacino

129 Which film had the slogan 'You haven't got a prayer'?

        a. Pet Semetary
        b. Creepshow
        c. The Unholy

130 In DAY OF THE DEAD, what was the domesticated zombie called?

        a. Chuck
        b. Bub
        c. Rob

131 In PHANTASM, what did The Tall Man's severed fingers turn into?

        a. A monstrous insect
        b. A rat
        c. A demon

132 In REVENGE OF FRANKENSTEIN, who was executed instead of Peter Cushing?

        a. A policeman
        b. A priest
        c. A thief

133 Who played Baron Frankenstein on the one occasion, for Hammer, in which Peter Cushing did not bring his considerable abilities to the role?

        a. Peter Davidson
        b. Ralph Bates
        c. John Hurt

134 Whose services did the Baron employ to revive his creation in THE EVIL OF FRANKENSTEIN?

        a. A doctor
        b. A vet
        c. A hypnotist

135 What was the name of the antique shop run by Peter Cushing in FROM BEYOND THE GRAVE?

        a. Temptations Ltd.
        b. Buy or Die
        c. Take Your Pick

136 In FRANKENSTEIN MUST BE DESTROYED, how was the body in the garden discovered?

        a. It was dug up by a dog
        b. A water main burst and pushed it to the surface
        c. A gardner found it

137 Who played the detective assigned to the series of bizarre murders in THE WOLFEN?

      a. Richard Burton

      b. Laurence Olivier

      c. Albert Finney

138 In INVASION OF THE BODY SNATCHERS, when did the aliens take over their human counterparts?

      a. As they made love

      b. As they slept

      c. As they ate

139 Which film warned 'Sleep Kills'?

      a. A Nightmare on Elm Street

      b. Night of the Demon

      c. Nightmares in a Damaged Brain

140 THE DEVIL RIDES OUT was based on a novel by which author?

      a. Harold Robbins

      b. Dennis Wheatley

      c. Robert E. Howard

141 Which film took as its basis the murderous exploits of David Berkowitz (Son of Sam)?

      a. Manhunter

      b. In Cold Blood

      c. Maniac

142 Dracula went to the Wild West in a 1958 film. Who did he meet there?

      a. Jesse James

      b. Wild Bill Hickock

      c. Billy the Kid

143 Frankenstein's Daughter did the same thing in a 1958 film. Who did *she* meet?

> a. General Custer
> b. Jesse James
> c. Pat Garrett

144 A doctor, obsessed with reptiles, gives his assistant constant injections of cobra venom until, at the climax of the film, the unfortunate assistant is transformed into a large snake. What was the film?

> a. Venom
> b. Cobra
> c. Ssssnake

145 Who was the father of ROSEMARY'S BABY?

> a. Satan
> b. A Demon
> c. A possessed rapist

146 Only one actor has ever played the Mummy, Dracula, the Frankenstein monster *and* a werewolf. Who was he?

> a. Boris Karloff
> b. Lon Chaney Jnr.
> c. John Carradine.

147 What was unusual about Christopher Lee's performance as Dracula in DRACULA, PRINCE OF DARKNESS?

> a. He wore a mask
> b. He wore gloves
> c. He didn't speak

148 How did Dracula meet his end in DRACULA HAS RISEN FROM THE GRAVE?

> a. Drowned in icy water
> b. Struck by lightning
> c. Impaled on a golden cross

149 He returned in TASTE THE BLOOD OF DRACULA. Who originally found his dried blood and took it?

> a. Ralph Bates
> b. Peter Sallis
> c. Roy Kinnear

150 What was the name of Dracula's hunchback assistant in SCARS OF DRACULA?

> a. Igor
> b. Klove
> c. Kurt

151 In DRACULA A.D. 1972, which part of London did Dracula return to?

> a. Piccadilly
> b. Wapping
> c. Chelsea

152 In THE SATANIC RITES OF DRACULA, what kind of plague did he intend unleashing upon the world?

> a. Herpes
> b. Cancer
> c. Bubonic plague

153 Which film bore the slogan 'When there's no more room in hell, the dead will walk the earth...'?

> a. Night of the Living Dead
> b. Zombie Flesh Eaters
> c. Dawn of the Dead

154 Robert Quarry played the part of an American Vampire in two films made in the early seventies. What was his name?

a. Count Kolchak
b. Count Yorga
c. Count Down

155 Who played RASPUTIN THE MAD MONK?

a. Vincent Price
b. Andre Morrell
c. Christopher Lee

156 In THE HOWLING, what was the name of the psychopathic killer finally revealed as a werewolf?

a. Eddie
b. Winston
c. Ronnie

157 How many investigators were hired to probe THE LEGEND OF HELL HOUSE?

a. Six
b. Eight
c. Four

158 In THE ENTITY, what horrific event happened to Barbara Hershey?

a. She was branded by a ghost
b. She was raped by a poltergeist
c. She was bitten by a werewolf

159 Which creature featured in OF UNKNOWN ORIGIN?

a. Rat
b. Wolf
c. Spider

160 Ray Milland played a wealthy plantation owner in this 1972 film, besieged by what kind of creature?

  a. Rattlesnakes
  b. Alligators
  c. Frogs

161 Which was the first Dracula film to be made in colour?

  a. Nosferatu
  b. Return of Dracula
  c. Dracula (1958)

162 Who, or what, was BEN?

  a. A dog
  b. A rat
  c. A cat

163 It was the sequel to a successful film called WILLARD, but what was the title of the book in which WILLARD had been based?

  a. Diary of a Ratman
  b. Ratmania
  c. Ratman's Notebooks

164 Which film had the slogan 'Be Afraid … Be Very Afraid'?

  a. Poltergeist
  b. The Fly
  c. Near Dark

165 The victims of the alien life-form in THE HIDDEN had a liking for a particular make of car. What was it?

  a. Rolls Royce
  b. Porsche
  c. Ferrari

166 Robert Powell goes for a job as head of a mental home and is introduced to the patients, each one of whom has a different story to tell but, at the end, he discovers that he is being shown around not by the retiring doctor he's to replace but by an escaped lunatic. What is the film?

      a. Madhouse
      b. Asylum
      c. Bedlam

167 In LUST FOR A VAMPIRE, what was the profession of the man who fell in love with beautiful bloodsucker Mircalla Karnstein?

      a. Doctor
      b. Writer
      c. Teacher

168 In TWINS OF EVIL, what was the fanatical group of witch-hunters led by Peter Cushing known as?

      a. The Organisation
      b. The Brotherhood
      c. The Fraternity

169 What did CAPTAIN KRONOS hunt in the 1972 film?

      a. Werewolves
      b. Zombies
      c. Vampires

170 Which film had the slogan 'In Space No One Can Hear You Scream'? (Yes, you've guessed it. No help on this one either . . .)

171 'Try Plaice, no one can steal your Bream' was the title of a film about a series of horrific murders in a fish and chip shop. True or false?

172 What was the subject matter which AUDREY ROSE concerned itself with?

        a. Telepathy
        b. Reincarnation
        c. Telekinesis

173 Where did the killers in DEATH LINE dwell?

        a. London's sewers
        b. London's Underground system
        c. London's buses

174 Who, or what, was LINK?

        a. A Computer
        b. A robot
        c. A chimpanzee

175 What were the names of the identical twins played by Jeremy Irons in DEAD RINGERS?

        a. Robert and Stephen
        b. Paul and John
        c. Elliott and Beverley

176 What did Charlton Heston find buried in the sand at the end of PLANET OF THE APES?

        a. The Empire State Building
        b. The Statue of Liberty
        c. The Eiffel Tower

177 What was the DEATH SHIP?

        a. A haunted Nazi freighter
        b. A galleon crewed by ghosts
        c. A plague ridden rowing boat

178 Who played THE PHANTOM OF THE OPERA in Hammer's 1962 remake? (The first and only film, you may or may not be interested to know, which ever gave me nightmares ... or at least the support film did!)

      a. Peter Cushing
      b. Herbert Lom
      c. Edward de Souza

179 THE QUATERMASS EXPERIMENT was originally a TV series. Who played Professor Quatermass on TV, in QUATERMASS AND THE PIT?

      a. Thorley Walters
      b. William Hartnell
      c. Andre Morrell

180 Who played him in the film version?

      a. William Franklin
      b. Brian Donleavy
      c. Andrew Kier

181 What was the nickname given to the mechanical shark by the crew of JAWS?

      a. Rustbucket
      b. Guts
      c. Bruce

182 Who wrote the novel on which FIRESTARTER was based?

      a. Stephen King
      b. Shaun Hutson
      c. James Herbert

183 Which film featured a pair of binoculars with spring loaded spikes for piercing the eyes of the victim?

      a. Peeping Tom
      b. Horrors of the Black Museum
      c. Torture Garden

184 What was the name of the group of men who told each other macabre tales in GHOST STORY?

      a. The Spinechillers
      b. The Spooks
      c. The Chowder Society

185 How did Vincent Price meet his death in WITCHFINDER GENERAL?

      a. Hacked to death with an axe
      b. Burned with a branding iron
      c. Torn apart with a meat hook

186 In HANDS OF THE RIPPER, who was Angharad Rees's father?

      a. Sherlock Holmes
      b. Jack the Ripper
      c. Dr Jekyll

187 Who were the duelling magicians in THE RAVEN (1963)?

      a. Vincent Price and Boris Karloff
      b. Peter Cushing and Christopher Lee
      c. Bela Lugosi and Lon Chaney Jnr.

188 Who won an Oscar for his portrayal of DR JEKYLL AND MR HYDE in 1932?

      a. Clark Gable
      b. Spencer Tracy
      c. Frederic March

189 How did Boris Karloff kill Bela Lugosi in THE BLACK CAT in 1933?

       a. Crushed him to death
       b. Flayed him alive
       c. Shot him

190 What were the two gimmicks designed to warn audiences of horrific moments in CHAMBER OF HORRORS in 1953?

       a. The Scare Counter and the Fear Factor
       b. The Terror Tone and the Fright Foghorn
       c. The Fear Flasher and the Horror Horn

191 Which well-known actor had one of his first parts as a gardener in the 1970 version of THE GHOUL?

       a. John Hurt
       b. Mel Gibson
       c. Tom Cruise

192 What was the name of Dr Phibes' adversary in DR PHIBES RISES AGAIN?

       a. Sieberbecke
       b. Biederbecke
       c. Birdy

193 Which film had the slogan 'Man is the warmest place to hide'?

       a. The Exorcist
       b. The Fly
       c. The Thing

194 John Cassavettes came to a spectacular end in THE FURY. What happened to him?

    a. He was torn apart by dogs

    b. He was blown to pieces by thought waves

    c. He was pulled into a combine harvester

195 Which 1957 film did critics demand be given an S.O. certificate standing for SADISTS ONLY?

    a. The Curse of Frankenstein

    b. The Blob

    c. Return of Dracula

196 What was the name of Dracula's deranged assistant in the 1931 version?

    a. Ridley

    b. Raymond

    c. Renfield

197 After his first spell as a werewolf, where, in AN AMERICAN WEREWOLF IN LONDON, did David Naughton wake up?

    a. In the grounds of Buckingham Palace

    b. In a cage at London Zoo

    c. At a circus

198 This H.G. Wells story was first filmed in 1931 with Charles Laughton, then again in the '70s with Burt Lancaster in the same role. What was the name of the character they played?

    a. Dr Death

    b. Dr Morton

    c. Dr Moreau

199 How many survivors did the space marines come upon in the devastated planet colony in ALIENS?

      a. Five
      b. Nine
      c. One

200 What was the name of the demon in THE EXORCIST?

      a. Beelzebub
      b. Pazuzu
      c. Behemoth

Cast Off…

Wow. Snappy section heading, eh? No? Oh, all right then.

A brief word of explanation might be in order at this stage. Having battled your way through over 700 questions so far, you'll be glad to know there's not too many more left. This next section struck me, or should I say the *idea* for it struck me while watching RAISING ARIZONA on TV one night. Now, why that particular film should spark me into thinking about this section I don't know, but that was when the idea came.

Some films are so famous that even to mention their cast list should be enough to jog memories. For instance, if I was to say: Anthony Perkins, Janet Leigh, Martin Balsam, John Gavin and Vera Miles, I realize that most people would immediately say PSYCHO and, of course, they'd be right. The same way as if I said: Richard Burton, Louise Fletcher, Linda Blair and Max Von Sydow, you'd all immediately shout 'a load of crap'. The answer is actually 'EXORCIST II' but the first answer would have been just as accurate.

So, that's what this section is. A mixture of films straight horror and urban horror, old and new, good and bad, which you have to identify solely by their casts. However, when I said that some films were so famous they could be identified by their casts, quite a few of the following are not exactly what you'd call famous, but then again, life's a bitch sometimes ...

Good luck.

1 Colin Clive, Elsa Lanchester, Boris Karloff and Ernest Thesiger.

        a. Frankenstein
        b. Bride of Frankenstein
        c. Son of Frankenstein

2 Gabriel Byrne, Albert Finney and Marcia Gay Hayden

        a. Siesta
        b. Shoot the Moon
        c. Miller's Crossing

3 Bela Lugosi, Dwight Frye, Edward Van Sloan and Helen Chandler

        a. Dracula's Daughter
        b. Dracula
        c. The Black Cat

4 William Holden, Ernest Borgnine, Robert Ryan, Warren Oates and Edmond O'Brien

        a. The Dirty Dozen
        b. The Mean Machine
        c. The Wild Bunch

5 John Hurt, Bridget Fonda, Raul Julia and Michael Hutchence

        a. Frankenstein Unbound
        b. Scandal
        c. Kiss of the Spiderwoman

6 Basil Rathbone, Boris Karloff, Bela Lugosi and Lionel Atwill

        a. Ghost of Frankenstein
        b. Son of Frankenstein
        c. The Hound of the Baskervilles

7 Kiefer Sutherland, Julia Roberts and Kevin Bacon

    a. Tremors
    b. Pretty Woman
    c. Flatliners

8 Gene Hackman, Roy Scheider, Fernando Rey and Tony Lo Bianco

    a. The French Connection
    b. French Connection II
    c. Narrow Margin

9 Christopher Walken, Helen Mirren, Natasha Richardson and Rupert Everett

    a. Another Country
    b. The Handmaid's Tale
    c. The Comfort of Strangers

10 Peter Cushing, Veronica Carlson, Simon Ward and Freddie Jones

    a. Frankenstein and the Monster From Hell
    b. Frankenstein Must Be Destroyed
    c. Frankenstein Created Woman

11 Keith Carradine, Powers Boothe, Fred Ward, Peter Coyote and Brion James

    a. 48 Hours
    b. Southern Comfort
    c. Extreme Prejudice

12 Sigourney Weaver, Tom Skerritt, Yaphet Kotto and Ian Holm

    a. Alien
    b. Aliens
    c. The Dead Zone

13 Mathew Modine, Melanie Griffith and Michael Keaton

      a. Memphis Belle
      b. Batman
      c. Pacific Heights

14 James Brolin, Margot Kidder, Rod Steiger and Don Stroud

      a. The Amityville Horror
      b. Doberman Patrol
      c. Sisters

15 Arnold Schwarzenegger, Sharon Stone and Ronny Cox

      a. Commando
      b. Total Recall
      c. Predator

16 Kevin Van Hentenryck, Terri Susan Smith and Beverley Bonner

      a. Basket Case
      b. Frankenhooker
      c. Basketcase 2

17 Bruce Willis, Bonnie Bedelia and Alexander Godunuv

      a. In Country
      b. Salem's Lot
      c. Die Hard

18 Burt Reynolds, Ronny Cox, Jon Voight and Ned Beatty

      a. Midnight Cowboy
      b. Deliverance
      c. Runaway Train

19 William Peterson, Tom Noonan, Brian Cox and Kim Griest

       a. Cousins
       b. Manhunter
       c. Robocop

20 John Travolta, Nancy Allen and John Lithgow

       a. Carrie
       b. The Fury
       c. Blow Out

21 Harrison Ford, Bonnie Bedelia, Raul Julia and Greta Scacchi

       a. Witness
       b. Presumed Innocent
       c. The Rookie

22 Karen Black, Oliver Reed and Bette Davis

       a. Burnt Offerings
       b. The Triple Echo
       c. Madame Sin

23 Mickey Rourke, Ellen Barkin and Lance Henrikson

       a. Desperate Hours
       b. Johnny Handsome
       c. Sea of Love

24 Sissy Spacek, John Travolta, William Katt, Nancy Allen and Amy Irving

       a. Carrie
       b. Blow Out
       c. The Fury

25 Peter Weller, Hector Elizondo, Richard Crenna and Meg Foster

        a. Leviathan
        b. The Abyss
        c. Deep Star Six

26 John Hurd, Nastassia Kinski, Malcolm McDowell and Annette O'Toole

        a. Blue Thunder
        b. Cat People
        c. To The Devil A Daughter

27 Mel Gibson, Michelle Pfeiffer, Kurt Russell and Raoul Julia

        a. Mad Max
        b. The Fabulous Baker Boys
        c. Tequila Sunrise

28 Malcolm McDowell, Adrienne Corri, Patrick Magee and David Prowse

        a. Vampire Circus
        b. Clockwork Orange
        c. Tales From the Crypt

29 Michael Douglas, Andy Garcia, Kim Cattrall and Takakura Ken

        a. Internal Affairs
        b. Black Rain
        c. The Yakuza

30 Dee Wallace, Christopher Stone and Ed Lauter

        a. The Howling
        b. Cujo
        c. Family Plot

31 Jack MacGowran, Alfie Bass, Sharon Tate, Ferdy Mayne and Terry Downs

      a. Dance of the Vampires
      b. Kiss of the Vampire
      c. Vampire's Kiss

32 Maren Jensen, Ernest Borgnine, Lisa Hartman, Lois Nettleton and Michael Berryman

      a. The Hills Have Eyes
      b. Deadly Friend
      c. Deadly Blessing

33 Ed Harris, Mary Elizabeth Mastrantonio and Michael Biehn

      a. Leviathan
      b. Deep Star Six
      c. The Abyss

34 Christopher Walken, Brooke Adam, Martin Sheen and Herbert Lom

      a. The Dead Zone
      b. Enigma
      c. Firestarter

35 Louise Fletcher, Jack Nicholson, Sydney Lassick and Will Sampson

      a. Orca, Killer Whale
      b. Carrie
      c. One Flew Over the Cuckoo's Nest

36 Michael Keaton, Kim Basinger, Jack Nicholson and Billy Dee Williams

      a. No Mercy
      b. Batman
      c. The Two Jakes

37 David Carradine, Sylvester Stallone, John Landis and Mary Woronov

        a. Lock Up

        b. Into the Night

        c. Death Race 2000

38 Mel Gibson, Danny Glover, Patsy Kensit and Joss Ackland

        a. Lethal Weapon

        b. Lethal Weapon 2

        c. Predator 2

39 Julie Christie, Fritz Weaver, Gerrit Graham and Berry Kroger

        a. Don't Look Now

        b. Creepshow

        c. Demonseed

40 Kurt Russell, Donald Pleasence, Adrienne Barbeau and Isaac Hayes

        a. The Mean Season

        b. Escape From New York

        c. Shaft

41 Nigel Terry, Cherie Lunghi, Nicol Williamson and Helen Mirren

        a. Excalibur

        b. The Sword and the Sorcerer

        c. Conan the Destroyer

42 Ellen Burstyn, Jason Miller, Max Von Sydow, Kitty Wynn, Linda Blair and Lee J. Cobb (No clues here I'm afraid . . .)

43 Adrienne Barbeau, Jamie Lee Curtis, Janet Leigh, Hal Holbrook and Nick Atkins
       a. Assault on Precinct 13
       b. The Fog
       c. Prince of Darkness

44 James Caan, Mandy Patinkin and Terence Stamp
       a. Violent Streets
       b. The Godfather
       c. Alien Nation

45 Fred Astaire, John Houseman, Melvyn Douglas and Douglas Fairbanks
       a. Ghost Story
       b. Rollerball
       c. The Haunting

46 Jeremy Irons, Genevieve Bujold and Shirley Douglas
       a. Reversal of Fortune
       b. Dead Ringers
       c. Coma

47 Jamie Lee Curtis, Donald Pleasence, Nancy Loomis, Dick Warlock and Charles Cyphers (Be careful on this one ...)
       a. Halloween
       b. Halloween 2
       c. The Fog

48 Demi Moore, Michael Biehn and Jurgen Prochnow
       a. Ghost
       b. Terminator
       c. The Seventh Sign

49 Dee Wallace, Patrick MacNee, Christopher Stone and Slim Pickens
- a. The Howling
- b. The Wolfen
- c. Cujo

50 Gabriel Byrne, Scott Glen and Ian McKellan
- a. Miller's Crossing
- b. The Keep
- c. Vampire's Kiss

51 Deborah Kerr, Peter Wyngarde, Michael Redgrave and Megs Jenkins
- a. The Haunting
- b. The Innocents
- c. Children of the Damned

52 Michael Douglas, Charlie Sheen, Martin Sheen and Daryl Hannah
- a. War of the Roses
- b. Apocalypse Now
- c. Wall Street

53 Roy Scheider, Richard Dreyfuss and Robert Shaw (No clues ...)

54 Peter Weller, Nancy Allen and Tom Noonan
- a. Robocop 2
- b. Robocop
- c. Manhunter

55 Mickey Rourke, Charlotte Rampling, Robert De Niro and Lisa Bonet

        a. Year of the Dragon
        b. Angel Heart
        c. Barfly

56 Katharine Ross, Sam Elliot, Charles Gray and Roger Daltrey

        a. The Devil Rides Out
        b. Ruby
        c. The Legacy

57 Mel Gibson, Tina Turner and Angry Anderson

        a. Mad Max
        b. Mad Max Beyond Thunderdome
        c. Mad Max 2

58 Kevin Costner, Sean Connery, Andy Garcia and Robert de Niro

        a. Scarface
        b. Married to The Mob
        c. The Untouchables

59 Anthony Hopkins, Ann Margret and Burgess Meredith

        a. Tommy
        b. The Good Father
        c. Magic

60 Kyle MacLachlan, Isabella Rossellini, Dennis Hopper and Dean Stockwell

        a. Wild At Heart
        b. Blue Velvet
        c. Eraserhead

61 David Bowie, Candy Clark, Rip Torn and Buck Henry

      a. The Man Who Fell To Earth
      b. The Man Who Would Be King
      c. The Man Who Haunted Himself

62 Paul Newman, Tom Cruise and Mary Elizabeth Mastrantonio

      a. The Hustler
      b. The Color of Money
      c. Top Gun

63 Richard Burton, Lee Remick, Lino Ventura and Gordon Jackson

      a. The Omen
      b. The Exorcist 2
      c. The Medusa Touch

64 Jon Voight, Eric Roberts, Rebecca de Mornay and John Ryan

      a. Midnight Cowboy
      b. Star '80
      c. Runaway Train

65 Arnold Schwarzenegger, Mako, Sandhal Bergman, James Earl Jones and Max Von Sydow

      a. Conan the Destroyer
      b. Dragonslayer
      c. Conan the Barbarian

66 Heather Langenkamp, John Saxon, Robert Englund and Ronee Blakely

      a. Nightmare on Elm Street
      b. Deathtrap
      c. Halloween

67 Arnold Schwarzenegger, Michael Biehn, Linda Hamilton, Paul Winfield and Lance Henrickson

     a. Total Recall
     b. The Terminator
     c. Commando

68 Charlton Heston, Anthony Zerbe, Rosalind Cash and Paul Koslo

     a. Soylent Green
     b. The Omega Man
     c. Planet of the Apes

69 John Getz, Dan Hedaya, Frances McDormand and M. Emmett Walsh

     a. Raising Arizona
     b. Miller's Crossing
     c. Blood Simple

70 Lee Remick, Gregory Peck, David Warner, Billie Whitelaw, Patrick Troughton and Leo McKern

     a. The Omen
     b. Time After Time
     c. Omen 2

71 Eddie Murphy, Nick Nolte, Brion James and James Remar

     a. 48 Hours
     b. Another 48 Hours
     c. Harlem Nights

72 Vincent Price, Barbara Steele, Luana Anders and John Kerr

     a. The Raven
     b. Black Sunday
     c. The Pit and the Pendulum

73 Sylvester Stallone, Richard Crenna, Brian Dennehy and Jack Starrett
- a. First Blood
- b. Lock Up
- c. Tango and Cash

74 Jobeth Williams, Craig T. Nelson, Heather O'Rourke and Beatrice Straight
- a. Poltergeist 3
- b. Poltergeist 2
- c. Poltergeist

75 Bob Hoskins, Helen Mirren, Eddie Constantine, Dave King and Geoff Thompson
- a. Villain
- b. Get Carter
- c. The Long Good Friday

76 Talia Shire, Robert Foxworth, Richard Dysart and Armand Assante
- a. Prophecy
- b. Kingdom of the Spiders
- c. I, the Jury

77 Al Pacino, Diane Keaton, Talia Shire, Andy Garcia and Sofia Coppolla
- a. The Godfather
- b. The Godfather Part II
- c. The Godfather Part III

78 Peter Fonda, Warren Oates, Loretta Swit, R.G. Armstrong and Jack Starrett

a. Easy Rider
b. Race With the Devil
c. Fighting Mad

79 James and Stacey Keach, David and Keith Carradine and Randy and Dennis Quaid
a. Southern Comfort
b. Extreme Prejudice
c. The Long Riders

80 James Caan, Maud Adams, John Beck, Moses Gunn and John Houseman
a. The Killer Elite
b. Rollerball
c. The Other Side of Midnight

81 Dustin Hoffman, Susan George, Del Henney, Peter Vaughn and David Warner
a. Rain Man
b. Dirty Mary, Crazy Larry
c. Straw Dogs

82 Piper Laurie, Stuart Whitman, Roger Davis and Janit Baldwin
a. Carrie
b. Ruby
c. Audrey Rose

83 Charles Bronson, Hope Lange, Vincent Gardenia and Stuart Margolin
a. Death Wish
b. Death Wish II
c. Death Wish III

84 Michael Ironside, Patrick McGoohan, Jennifer O'Neill and Stephen Lack

      a. Watchers
      b. Scanners
      c. Looker

85 Marlon Brando, Martin Sheen, Frederic Forrest, G.D. Spradlin, Dennis Hopper and Robert Duvall (No clues here . . .)

86 Jack Nicholson, Shelley Duvall, Danny Lloyd and Scatman Crothers

      a. The Twilight Zone
      b. The Shining
      c. The Terror

87 Robert De Niro, Christopher Walken, Meryl Streep, John Cazale and John Savage

      a. Heaven's Gate
      b. Once Upon a Time in America
      c. The Deer Hunter

88 Charlton Heston, Leigh Taylor Young, Joseph Cotton and Edward G. Robinson

      a. The Omega Man
      b. Soylent Green
      c. Beneath the Planet of the Apes

89 Peter Finch, Faye Dunaway, William Holden and Robert Duvall

      a. Sunday, Bloody Sunday
      b. Bonnie and Clyde
      c. Network

90 Joan Collins, Sir John Gielgud, Richard Greene, Patrick Magee, Peter Cushing and Nigel Patrick

       a. Vault of Horror
       b. Tales That Witness Madness
       c. Tales from the Crypt

91 James Coburn, Maximilian Schell, David Warner, James Mason and Senta Berger

       a. Major Dundee
       b. Cross of Iron
       c. The Last Hard Men

92 Vincent Price, Diana Rigg, Sir Michael Hordern, Robert Morley, Arthur Lowe and Ian Hendry

       a. Asylum
       b. Theatre of Blood
       c. From Beyond the Grave

93 Oliver Reed, Vanessa Redgrave, Dudley Sutton, Michael Gothard and Georgina Hale

       a. The Rainbow
       b. Women in Love
       c. The Devils

94 Kurt Russell, Richard Dysart, T.K. Carter, A. Wilford Brimley and Keith David

       a. Escape From New York
       b. The Thing
       c. Starman

95 Ernest Borgnine, Lee Marvin, Charles Bronson, Telly Savalas, Clint Walker and Jim Brown

a. The Wild Bunch
b. The Dirty Dozen
c. The Professionals

96 James Woods, Deborah Harry, Sonja Smits and Les Carlson

a. The Fly
b. The Boost
c. Videodrome

97 Tom Baker, Anna Massey, Denholm Elliot, Terry Thomas, Daniel Massey and Curt Jurgens

a. Vault of Horror
b. Tales From the Crypt
c. Torture Garden

98 Christopher Lee, Edward Woodward, Ingrid Pitt, Britt Ekland and Diane Cilento

a. Dracula
b. The Wicker Man
c. House of the Long Shadows

99 Boris Karloff, John Carradine, George Zucco, Lon Chaney Jnr. and Glenn Strange

a. House of Dracula
b. House of Frankenstein
c. Abbott and Costello Meet Frankenstein

100 Christopher Plummer, James Mason, Anthony Quayle, David Hemmings, Susan Clark and Genevieve Bujold

a. Time After Time
b. Hands of the Ripper
c. Murder by Decree

In With A Shout...

The shout line, as it is called by those in the trade, is the slogan which appears on cinema posters to alert the viewers to the possible delights to be seen on the screen. Shout lines are used in every sphere of the media and the entertainment business to attract the public. The equivalent of a comedian's catchphrase, if you like, or a slogan used to sell soap powder. Instead of the usual ad-man's slogan of 'washing whiter than white' (a bit of an abstract concept that, I've always thought. A bit like saying a new soap cleans your skin so thoroughly you can see your bones ...) I've always preferred the idea of soap powder being pushed in the following way: Harassed housewife holds up clean shirt and packet of soap powder and announces to camera: 'Suds soap powder. It's bloody amazing.' Now that's *my* kind of advertising ...

However, I digress. Back to cinema shout lines. With horror films in particular, especially during the 50s and 60s, shout lines seemed to consist of challenges to the audience such as 'Dare you see this film' or 'Watch it with someone brave', or something along those lines. This verbal equivalent of throwing down the gauntlet sometimes worked, but nine times out of ten a truer reflection of the picture involved would have been a shout line reading: 'Make sure someone else has paid and you're not wasting your own money'.

The shout line is the province of the ad-man and when you consider that most ad-men's grip on reality is roughly equivalent to someone who's dropped some bad acid, then you'll understand why so many films suffer from such hysterical shout lines. However, there have been some good ones (and some bad), a selection of which you'll find in this section. The most famous of recent years was the one for ALIEN (already mentioned earlier in another section), the wonderfully simple 'In Space No One Can Hear You Scream'. I remember seeing ALIEN two days after it was released and thinking that they should have added something to that shout line such as: 'In Space No One Can Hear You Scream ... But try screaming in a darkened cinema and see what happens ...' The reason I mention this is because a lady sitting a couple of seats in front of me was busy demolishing an ice cream cone when the embryonic alien decided to burst from John Hurt's chest. She simultaneously shrieked at the top of her voice and hurled the cornet into the air only for it to plummet to earth like some kind of unguided missile, missing the lap of the bloke behind her by inches.

Don't you just love audience participation films?

Anyway, on with this section, and the scoring is the same as usual. Identify the film by its shout line alone and, for every correct answer, score one point.

1 The Strangest Love Story Ever Known

      a. Dracula

      b. Frankenstein

      c. The Mummy

2 She was the first . . .

      a. Psycho

      b. Jaws

      c. Maniac

3 They're Here . . .

      a. Poltergeist

      b. Poltergeist 2

      c. Poltergeist 3

4 They're Back . . .

      a. Gremlins

      b. Poltergeist 3

      c. Poltergeist 2

5 Be Very, Very Afraid . . .

      a. The Fly

      b. The Thing

      c. The Fly II

6 You Have Been Warned . . .

      a. The Exorcist

      b. The Omen

      c. Invasion of the Bodysnatchers

7 Suspense. Excitement. Adventure on every level . . .

      a. The Towering Inferno

      b. Die Hard

      c. The Lift

8 Together. The Screen's Titans of Terror . . .

      a. House of Frankenstein
      b. House of Dracula
      c. House of the Long Shadows

9 The director of 'The French Connection' is back on the streets again . . .

      a. The Guardian
      b. To Live and Die in L.A.
      c. Rampage

10 Imagine your worst nightmare a reality . . .

      a. The Howling
      b. The Hunger
      c. Miracle Mile

11 Pay to Get in, Pray to Get out . . .

      a. My Bloody Valentine
      b. The Ghost Train
      c. The Funhouse

12 The Night *He* Came Home

      a. Hell Night
      b. Halloween
      c. Halloween 2

13 He loved the American dream, with a vengeance . . .

      a. Goodfellas
      b. The Untouchables
      c. Scarface

14 Real power can't be given, it must be taken . . .

      a. Black Rain
      b. The Godfather III
      c. Internal Affairs

15 Osaka, Japan. A Killer on the Loose. A Conspiracy on the Rise. A Cop on the Edge ...

> a. The Yakuza
> b. Black Rain
> c. Enter the Dragon

16 1964, When America was at war with itself ...

> a. Mississippi Burning
> b. The Klansman
> c. Southern Comfort

17 Two bodies. Two minds. One soul ...

> a. Sisters
> b. Dead Ringers
> c. Twins

18 Man is the Warmest Place to Hide ...

> a. The Exorcist
> b. Invasion of the Body Snatchers
> c. The Thing

19 Three decades of life in the Mafia ...

> a. The Godfather
> b. Goodfellas
> c. Bugsy

20 In the not too distant future wars will no longer exist, but there will be ...

> a. Death Race 2000
> b. Turkey Shoot
> c. Rollerball

21 The future of law enforcement ...

a. Robocop
b. Trancers
c. Total Recall

22 Who lit the fuse that blew Harold's world apart...?
    a. Nighthawks
    b. The Long Good Friday
    c. Violent Streets

23 A New Name for Terror...
    a. Cujo
    b. Incubus
    c. Shivers

24 Sleep kills...
    a. Bad Dreams
    b. Nightmare on Elm Street
    c. Nightmares

25 Nine men who came too late and stayed too long...
    a. The Professionals
    b. Ulzana's Raid
    c. The Wild Bunch

26 On the Eastern Front in 1943 the German soldiers were no longer fighting for ideals. They were fighting for their lives...
    a. The Dirty Dozen
    b. Cross of Iron
    c. Casualties of War

27 The lucky ones died first...

     a. Zombie Flesh Eaters
     b. Deadly Friend
     c. The Hills Have Eyes

28 Their thoughts can kill ...

     a. The Fury
     b. Scanners
     c. The Brood

29 First it possesses your mind, then it destroys your body ...

     a. Shivers
     b. Rabid
     c. Videodrome

30 A Rock and Roll Fable ...

     a. Tommy
     b. Streets of Fire
     c. The Wall

Once Upon A Time...

A young man lives an almost hermit-like existence, running a seedy motel and living, apparently, with his mother in a Gothic mansion overlooking the motel. However, he is psychotic and periodically dresses up as his mother to murder anyone who threatens him ...

No need to go any further is there?

The plot of PSYCHO, in a nutshell (or *case*, however you want to look at it). The plots of many films can be summarized in a few lines (some, like ZOMBIE FLESH EATERS, can be summarized using just single words, most of them derogatory). Good plots will trigger the memories without even the mention of an actor's or actress's name.

So, you have the idea for the next section.

The plots of films both famous and not quite so famous will be summarized in a few lines; just identify the films. Scoring, as usual, is one point for every correct answer.

1 A disfigured musician, whose wife has been accidentally killed during an operation, seeks vengeance against the doctors who he blames for her death by using modified versions of the Plagues of Israel to wipe them out.

> a. Theatre of Blood
> b. The Abominable Dr Phibes
> c. Vault of Horror

2 Lured to a distant planet by a fake distress signal, the crew of a spaceship are systematically slaughtered by the monstrous organism they have inadvertantly brought aboard.

> a. It! The Terror from Beyond Space
> b. Leviathan
> c. Alien

3 A scientist experimenting with evolutionary theories accidentally transforms himself into an ape-like creature after regressing in a submersion tank.

> a. The Wolfman
> b. Altered States
> c. The Island of Dr Moreau

4 A family move into a large house which they buy for an artificially low price, only to discover that it was the scene of a mass murder a year earlier and still contains many evil spirits, one of which possesses the husband and threatens to cause the same mass murder to be repeated.

> a. Poltergeist
> b. The Haunting
> c. The Amityville Horror

5 Two young men on a tour of Europe are attacked on the Yorkshire moors by a monstrous creature, resulting in living death for one of them and something even more unspeakable for the survivor.

> a. The Howling
> b. An American Werewolf in London
> c. The Wolfen

6 A film sound man accidentally tapes the murder of a politician and finds himself sucked into a conspiracy aimed at killing both him and the girl who had been with the politician at the time of his death.

> a. Blow Out
> b. Blow Up
> c. Blow Job

7 Two separated siamese twins remain together despite the homicidal tendencies of the smaller of them. He is protected by his more normal brother who lures victims to his horribly deformed sibling and finally becomes a victim himself.

> a. Twins
> b. Dead Ringers
> c. Basketcase

8 Nazi doctor Joseph Mengele leaves his hideaway in South America to initiate a diabolical scheme devised during the war, involving a cloning process. Mengele is tracked down by a determined Jewish Nazi hunter who finally corners him at the house of one of his creations where the final bloody confrontation takes place.

> a. Marathon Man
> b. The Boys From Brazil
> c. Triumph of the Spirit

9 A young woman, offered a room for the night in a castle, releases a young man from chains despite the pleadings of his mother and finds that she has unleashed a reign of terror on the countryside and, in particular, the girls' school where she has gone to teach.

    a. Suspiria
    b. Kiss of the Vampire
    c. Brides of Dracula

10 An earth tremor releases a particularly malevolent strain of cockroach from the earth, creatures that feed on carbon and can create fire and which are finally cross-bred with normal cockroaches to create a horrific cannibalistic hybrid.

    a. Tremors
    b. Bug
    c. Squirm

11 A young girl, shunned and ridiculed by her schoolmates, finally takes terrible revenge on them using her telekinetic powers after she's been horribly humiliated at the school prom night.

    a. Ruby
    b. Prom Night
    c. Carrie

12 A car seems to take on a life of its own, and also to infect all who own it with evil, from its first day on a production line to its subsequent restoration by a bullied boy who, under the influence of the car, becomes a violent individual.

    a. The Car
    b. Road Games
    c. Christine

13 A young woman, victim of an age-old curse, dares not lose her virginity for fear of turning into a black panther, something which she can also do when enraged.

     a. Cat People
     b. Curse of the Cat People
     c. Catwoman

14 Patients in for supposedly routine operations are actually being used as unwitting organ donors in a conspiracy amongst top ranking doctors in a Chicago hospital. The horrific scheme is exposed by two young doctors whose lives are threatened.

     a. Visiting Hours
     b. Coma
     c. Halloween 2

15 In Victorian England two scientists try to discover the origin of a huge skeleton believed to be a missing link of some kind, but one of them wants to steal the findings and make himself famous despite the efforts of the other to find a cure for madness, perfected by using the creature's blood.

     a. I, Monster
     b. The Blood Beast Terror
     c. The Creeping Flesh

16 An adulterous woman and her young son are trapped in their car and menaced by a rabid dog.

     a. Cujo
     b. The Pack
     c. Zoltan, Hound of Dracula

17 A peasant, kept caged like an animal for years, rapes a servant girl who finally gives birth to a child who grows up to become a werewolf in sixteenth-century Spain.

a. Frankenstein Meets The Wolfman
b. The Wolfman
c. Curse of the Werewolf

18 In a small American town the undertaker re-animates dead bodies, recreating their original looks and causing them to turn into killers, until he is discovered by the town sheriff who finds that he himself is in for a rather nasty shock.

a. Dead and Buried
b. Dawn of the Dead
c. Re-animator

19 A schoolteacher recovers from a four-year coma to discover that he has acquired the power to look into people's pasts and futures and sees, by meeting a politician, possible nuclear war.

a. Prophecy
b. The Sender
c. The Dead Zone

20 A couple are in Venice trying to cope with the death of their young daughter when the husband realizes he has the gift of second sight and is inadvertently drawn into a confrontation with a murderer.

a. The Comfort of Strangers
b. Don't Look Now
c. Ghost Story

21 A writer, injured in a car crash, is nursed back to health by one of his biggest fans who then demands that he write a book just for her and threatens him with everything ranging from needles to sledgehammers.

a. The Fan
b. Postcards from the Edge
c. Misery

22 Three depraved men seeking even greater thrills fall under the spell of a warped aristocrat who promises he will, with their help, resuscitate a being of immense evil.

a. The Devil Rides Out
b. Taste the Blood of Dracula
c. The Hell Fire Club

23 Five youngsters travel to a secluded cabin where they discover a tape recording and an ancient book telling how to raise demons. Subsequently, a number of them become possessed, leaving one individual to battle the forces of evil alone.

a. The Exorcist 3
b. The Hills Have Eyes
c. The Evil Dead

24 A photographer finds that she has the ability to pick out, from those she has photographed, murder victims and finds her own life at risk when the killer realizes her ability.

a. The Eyes of Laura Mars
b. Victims
c. Blow Up

25 A small Californian town is threatened by a group of ghostly lepers seeking revenge against the descendants of those who sent them to their deaths one hundred years before.

a. Dawn of the Dead
b. The Fog
c. The Serpent and the Rainbow

26 Four teenagers spend the night in a fairground during which time they witness a murder and are then pursued by a horrific mutant which kills them one by one.

     a. Fright Night
     b. Friday the 13th
     c. The Funhouse

27 A futuristic holiday resort offers its customers the chance to dress up and act like cowboys, but when something goes wrong the death toll rises alarmingly.

     a. Futureworld
     b. Westworld
     c. The Ultimate Warrior

28 A thirty foot long creature is captured by fishermen off the coast of Ireland but it turns out to be the offspring of a much larger animal which, when its baby is exhibited in London, turns up to reclaim its young and simultaneously destroys the capital.

     a. Gorgo
     b. Godzilla
     c. Gidrah

29 In a Transylvanian village a number of people are found turned to stone. A local brain surgeon and a professor try to find the answers but for different reasons.

     a. The Trollenberg Terror
     b. The Gorgon
     c. Transylvania 6-5000

30 Twenty-three years after being locked up in a lunatic asylum, a maniac killer returns to his home town seeking revenge.

     a. Halloween 2
     b. Halloween
     c. Psycho

31 A mask-maker decides to punish the children of America and so manufactures masks which kill when worn. A doctor tries to stop the terrible plan from materializing.

> a. Halloween 3
> b. Masque of the Red Death
> c. Mask

32 A mysterious stranger arrives in a Western town, paints every building red, renames the place Hell then waits for the arrival of three outlaws who murdered the sheriff of the town years earlier.

> a. The Good, the Bad and the Ugly
> b. A Fistful of Dollars
> c. High Plains Drifter

33 A woman newscaster on the trail of a psychopathic killer discovers the truth about him, almost dying in the process but her ordeal only gets worse when she is sent to a secluded resort to rest.

> a. The Wolfen
> b. The Howling
> c. Werewolf in a Girl's Dormitory

34 A woman discovers, to her horror, that the man she has married is in fact a space alien masquerading as her real-life husband.

> a. Bride of the Monster
> b. Not of this Earth
> c. I Married a Monster from Outer Space

35 Four psychic investigators are sent to a site to check out the validity of a haunting and discover that the evil force there is far more malevolent than they could ever have imagined.

        a. The Innocents
        b. The Legend of Hell House
        c. The Amityville Horror

36 After using a new fertility drug, a woman gives birth to a vampire baby which, after slaughtering the medical staff present at its birth, escapes into the sewers of New York.

        a. Embryo
        b. It's Alive
        c. Son of Dracula

37 A young man goes to live with his uncle who is convinced the youth is a vampire but, even though he has a taste for blood, we are never really sure if his vampiric tendencies are real or imagined.

        a. Patrick
        b. Martin
        c. Vampire's Kiss

38 A returning space probe reactivates the dead, turning them into cannibalistic zombies. A small group of human survivors are trapped and besieged in a lonely house by the flesh-eating creatures.

        a. Invasion of the Body Snatchers
        b. The Quatermass Experiment
        c. Night of the Living Dead

39 The last living human survivor of a germ war lives in a deserted Los Angeles where he continually plays a deadly cat and mouse game with the mutated homicidal survivors of the infection. During the day he tries to kill them, at night they come for him.

        a. The Last Man on Earth
        b. The Omega Man
        c. Chosen Survivors

40 The Antichrist is reborn and infiltrated into the family of an American politician. (No clues this time I'm afraid . . .)

41 A party of schoolgirls from an Australian school encounter terror during an outing, the whole traumatic episode ending with abductions and suicide.
>   a. Just Before Dawn
>   b. Picnic at Hanging Rock
>   c. Campsite Massacre

42 An English landowner, with knowledge of voodoo, uses the recently dead of his Cornish town as slave labour to work in his mine.
>   a. Dawn of the Dead
>   b. I Walked with a Zombie
>   c. Plague of the Zombies

43 A young woman, whose father tried to steal the secret of eternal life from a tribe in Borneo, is cursed with an affliction which sees her periodically turning into a monster.
>   a. The Reptile
>   b. Cry of the Werewolf
>   c. The Creeping Flesh

44 A family discover that their house was built on the site of a cemetery and are menaced by the malevolent spirits unleashed because of this desecration.
>   a. The Amityville Horror
>   b. Poltergeist
>   c. The House of the Cemetery

45 An object, thought to be an unexploded bomb, is found amidst the ruins of a disused London tube station but, upon further examination, it is revealed as having a far more horrific origin.

      a. Quatermass and the Pit
      b. Twenty Million Miles to Earth
      c. Death Line

46 Two couples on a camping holiday in southern America are pursued by satanists when the two men accidentally witness a ritual sacrifice.

      a. The Mephisto Waltz
      b. Running Scared
      c. Race with the Devil

47 In the future when all poverty, illness and war has been abolished, the only way of appeasing the masses is with an incredibly violent spectator sport.

      a. The Ultimate Warrior
      b. Death Race 2000
      c. Rollerball

48 In a New York apartment a young couple find themselves involved with witchcraft and, after a series of horrific nightmares, the wife discovers she is pregnant with the Devil himself. (No clues again . . .)

49 A failed writer takes a job as caretaker at a hotel for the winter but in the claustrophobic atmosphere he begins to go insane, haunted by visions of the previous caretaker and other guests.

      a. Dead of Night
      b. The Shining
      c. The Haunting

50 A young woman moves into an apartment block inhabited by what turn out to be the ghosts of dead murderers, discovering also that the apartment block forms the gateway to Hell itself.

     a. Rosemary's Baby
     b. Ghost Story
     c. The Sentinel

51 A family on a camping holiday are systematically murdered by a group of cannibalistic fiends who have survived for years by living off others unfortunate enough to pass through their territory.

     a. Mirage
     b. The Hills Have Eyes
     c. The Texas Chainsaw Massacre

52 Twelve men on an Antarctic research base are menaced by a monstrous alien with the ability to absorb them. (You're on your own with this one too ...)

53 A pathologist discovers what he thinks is materialized 'fright' and sets out to capture a specimen of the creature responsible for causing people to die of fright.

     a. Shivers
     b. The Tingler
     c. The Fiend without a Face

54 A cable TV producer, ever on the look-out for more outrageous programmes, discovers one which shocks even him. But, shock gives way to horror when he finds out that it is a front for a subversive group who plan to use *him* in their schemes.

     a. Network
     b. Switching Channels
     c. Videodrome

55 A shy young man, dominated by his bed-ridden mother, befriends the rat he is meant to destroy and gradually breeds more and more, using them against those he hates.

   a. The Rats
   b. Ben
   c. Willard

56 A series of horrific murders, originally thought to be the work of terrorists, is finally discovered to be the work of a force far more powerful and deadly. A detective and a reporter battle the forces of evil.

   a. Helter Skelter
   b. The Howling
   c. The Wolfen

57 A young boy is menaced by a malevolent doll which becomes possessed by the spirit of a dead murderer. The lethal toy then tries to enter the boy's body, killing all those who try to stop it.

   a. Child's Play
   b. Children Shouldn't Play With Dead Things
   c. The Devil Doll

58 Five medical students decide to see if there is anything beyond death and, one by one, each of them volunteers to be medically 'dead', enabling them to experience the after-life.

   a. Ghost
   b. Flatliners
   c. From Beyond the Grave

59 A brilliant scientist is apparently killed by gangsters when his laboratory is blown up but, using the techniques of skin regeneration he'd been working on before, he survives and sets about avenging himself on them.

     a. Dr X
     b. Doc Savage
     c. Darkman

60 The crew of a deep sea salvage ship discover the wreck of a Russian ship and unwittingly unleash a creature which slaughters them one by one.

     a. Deep Star Six
     b. The Abyss
     c. Leviathan

61 A couple looking for a nanny to mind their baby are horrified to discover that the woman who comes for the job is an agent of evil, able to control the forces of nature and prepared to sacrifice their child as she has others in her care.

     a. The Nanny
     b. The Guardian
     c. Hush, Hush Sweet Charlotte

62 In a small American town, people begin dying mysteriously but only the local doctor suspects the truth. A truth which finally involves him facing his own worst nightmare.

     a. Arachnophobia
     b. Kingdom of the Spiders
     c. The Giant Spider Invasion

63 A mass murderer finds how to harness the power of electricity for his own means and escapes the electric chair, but a young man finds he can locate and identify the killer in his dreams, so the killer comes looking for *him*.

      a. Nightmare on Elm Street
      b. Shocker
      c. In Cold Blood

64 A man discovers, accidentally, that America is to be attacked by Russian nuclear missiles and that he has less than fifty minutes before the first one lands. He tries to persuade those around him that he is telling the truth as armageddon looms nearer.

      a. When the Wind Blows
      b. Threads
      c. Miracle Mile

65 A time warp catapults a scientist from the 21st century back to Victorian times where he meets a doctor who is obsessed with creating life from dead bodies and has, indeed, already created a monster which is terrorising the countryside.

      a. Frankenstein 1970
      b. Frankenstein Unbound
      c. Frankenstein: The True Story

66 Two newlyweds, desperate to pay their mortgage decide to let their spare room to an apparently sophisticated lodger who turns out to be a psychopath.

      a. The Tenant
      b. The Lodger
      c. Pacific Heights

67 A female cop in Los Angeles' becomes the object of a killer's fantasy after he sees her kill an armed robber during a hold-up. Only gradually does she realize that the man she has come to love is actually a maniac.

> a. Angel
> b. Chains of Gold
> c. Blue Steel

68 A horribly disfigured criminal is persuaded to do a robbery and is double-crossed and imprisoned, but while in prison he undergoes surgery to alter his features and, upon release, he goes hunting for the two colleagues who double-crossed him.

> a. Johnny Handsome
> b. The Getaway
> c. Revenge

69 A much respected and highly decorated Russian submarine Captain sets sail for America in a brand new submarine but neither side knows whether he wants to start World War Three or defect. A CIA agent is the only one who can discover the truth.

> a. Run Silent, Run Deep
> b. The Hunt for Red October
> c. Red Storm Rising

70 A young American, passionately devoted to his country, enlists in the army and is horrifically wounded in the Vietnam War, returning to find that the ideals he fought for are unimportant to ordinary people and even to the other crippled veterans with whom he shares his life.

> a. Platoon
> b. Hamburger Hill
> c. Born on the Fourth of July

71 Police in New York discover that a killer is finding victims through the personal column of a newspaper. A detective masquerades as a 'lonely heart' in order to trap the killer.

> a. Sea of Love
> b. Presumed Innocent
> c. Blue Steel

72 Two New York cops are forced to escort a Japanese killer back to Osaka where he escapes and they find themselves up against not only a different culture but also a conspiracy.

> a. The Yakuza
> b. Black Rain
> c. Enter the Dragon

73 A schoolteacher and his wife move into a new house close to a busy road and are finally shown, by one of the locals, a place where the dead can be brought back to life. Something which comes in handy for the husband when their son is killed by a truck.

> a. Re-Animator
> b. Pet Sematary
> c. Return of the Living Dead

74 An abrasive media celebrity finds that his show isn't as important as he thought it was and that, perhaps, he should have put more effort into his marriage, finally discovering that people might be willing to kill him for his views.

> a. Network
> b. Broadcast News
> c. Talk Radio

75 Rendered quadriplegic by a car accident, a man is given a highly intelligent, highly trained rhesus monkey to do everyday jobs for him but finds that the animal is beginning to act against those he dislikes and also that he cannot control its violent impulses.

> a. Link
> b. Monkey Shines
> c. Greystoke

76 An FBI investigator comes out of self-imposed retirement to help track down a murderer who specializes in slaughtering entire families in their houses. In order to help him in his pursuit of the killer, the FBI man enlists the aid of a psychopathic psychiatrist whom he was responsible for catching two years earlier.

> a. The Silence of the Lambs
> b. Manhunter
> c. In Cold Blood

77 Led by a crazed army colonel, three convicts break into, and take control of, a nuclear missile silo and threaten to launch three Titan missiles at Russia unless their demands are met.

> a. The Dirty Dozen
> b. Wargames
> c. Twilight's Last Gleaming

78 A policeman, in Los Angeles for Christmas to see his wife and children, finds himself unwittingly caught up in a terrorist bid to steal 600 million dollars' worth of bearer bonds from the vaults of the office block where he is.

> a. Lethal Weapon
> b. Die Hard
> c. Dirty Harry

79 A number of apparently normal citizens go crazy, stealing Ferraris and murdering people because they've been possessed by an alien organism which is being hunted by another alien in human form who teams up with a sceptical detective to solve the series of crimes.

> a. They Live
> b. Invasion of the Bodysnatchers
> c. The Hidden

80 A married man has a fling with a woman from a publishing company and finds that she is not as ready to call a halt to the relationship as *he* is. Mayhem ensues. (No clues here ...)

81 A team of mercenaries in the South American jungle find that they themselves have been chosen as victims by a life form from outer space which kills them one by one for sport.

> a. Open Season
> b. Predator
> c. Predator 2

82 A policeman is shot and fatally wounded but doctors and scientists manage to keep him alive using mechanical parts and end up transforming him into a powerful creation to replace Detroit's striking police force.

> a. Terminator
> b. Android
> c. Robocop

83 An habitual criminal and a policewoman fall in love and marry only to discover they can't have children so they steal one of a set of quins only to be pursued by a vengeful bounty hunter.

a. Who Will Love My Children?
b. Raising Arizona
c. Family Plot

84 Four men decide to go on a camping and canoeing trip for one last time on a river which is about to be dammed but, when they crash the rapids and run into some murderous hillbillies, the trip turns into a nightmare.

a. Southern Comfort
b. Deliverance
c. No Mercy

85 A forger kills the partner of a policeman and finds that he is then pursued by the policeman and his new partner who will stop at nothing to get him, even going so far as to rob and cause the death of an FBI man in order to trap the forger.

a. King of the City
b. 48 Hours
c. To Live and Die in L.A.

86 A psychiatrist is called to a convent to investigate the murder of a new born baby which has apparently been given birth to by one of the young nuns. Was it immaculate conception or the product of normal illicit sex and did she murder the child or did it die normally? The psychiatrist must find out the answers.

a. Psycho III
b. Agnes of God
c. The Shoes of the Fisherman

87 A Cuban arrives in America and gradually fights his way up from small-time hood to drug baron, his dealings with drugs finally causing his very bloody demise.

a. Chains of Gold
b. The Godfather 2
c. Scarface

88 A Vietnam veteran returns to America to find only antagonism and hatred against him to the point where, after being wrongly imprisoned, he finally sets off on a violent path of revenge against those who wronged him.

a. The Exterminator
b. First Blood
c. Taxi Driver

89 Nine Louisiana national guardsmen in the swamps on manoeuvres antagonize the local population and end up being hunted and killed one by one by the people who live in the swamps.

a. The Hills Have Eyes
b. Just Before Dawn
c. Southern Comfort

90 During the Second World War a detachment of German soldiers in a castle in the Carpathian mountains are systematically slaughtered. The SS are sent for to quell what is thought to be partisan activity but the real cause is eventually revealed as something far more malevolent.

a. The Keep
b. Castle Keep
c. The Haunted Palace

91 A washed-up cop is sent to Las Vegas to pick up a witness who is meant to testify against the Mafia in an impending trial. He finds that his efforts to return the witness are thwarted at every turn, and the further he goes, the more he realizes that he has uncovered a conspiracy involving police and Mafia.

    a. The Rookie
    b. Honor Thy Father
    c. The Gauntlet

92 A man sees his best friend killed by a street gang and swears vengeance. He arms himself with an assortment of weapons and sets off on a one-man campaign of vengeance finally discovering that he is also up against organized crime. Undeterred he fights on, finally putting the gang boss through a meat grinder.

    a. Death Wish 3
    b. Trackdown
    c. The Exterminator

93 A warped psychiatrist dresses up as a woman to kill any of the patients that his male personality takes a fancy to. A prostitute and the son of a murdered woman team up to catch him.

    a. Dressed to Kill
    b. Sisters
    c. The Fury

94 A family of psychopaths systematically slaughter and torture five teenagers foolish enough to stop off at their house, using the bodies to make sausages and other cuts of meat. A girl, driven mad by her ordeal, manages to escape.

    a. Corruption
    b. The Hills Have Eyes
    c. The Texas Chainsaw Massacre

95 In the Deep South of America a man runs a hotel, using it as a front for his murderous activities. The guests he kills he feeds to his pet crocodile which eventually claims him as a victim, too.

a. Deathtrap
b. Deadly Blessing
c. Vengeance; the Demon

96 A young American is caught in possession of cannabis and given a life sentence in a nightmarish Turkish prison from which he eventually escapes. (You're on your own again . . .)

97 The story of the Manson family's murderous killing spree against Hollywood's rich and famous in the late sixties.

a. In Cold Blood
b. Helter Skelter
c. The Family

98 A motorist, for no apparent reason, is pursued by a truck driver who is, by turns, awkward, dangerous then murderous.

a. White Line Fever
b. Two Lane Blacktop
c. Duel

99 An unbalanced TV newsman announces that he's going to commit suicide on the air and his ratings suddenly soar. Seeing the effect such a gimmick has had on viewing figures, his company allow him on every week to rant and rave about the problems he sees until, finally, he becomes a thorn in their side.

a. Network
b. Switching Channels
c. Broadcast News

100 A Vietnam veteran, disgusted by the corruption he sees around him is finally tipped over the edge by the discovery of a twelve-year-old prostitute whom he tries to rescue. His obsession with her leads to a horrific killing spree. (Guess what? No clues here either ...)

101 On the Eastern Front in 1943, a German platoon acquires a new and idealistic Captain whose background and views bring him into immediate, murderous, conflict with the platoon sergeant.

      a. From Hell to Eternity
      b. Cross of Iron
      c. Empire of the Sun

102 A would-be runner discovers that his brother is mixed up with both the CIA and a group of Nazis and that knowledge is enough to push him into the clutches of the leading Nazi who uses his particular skills to devastatingly awful effect trying to glean information from the innocent brother.

      a. Marathon Man
      b. The Boys From Brazil
      c. Fair Trade

103 A young woman is raped by a concert pianist who lives in the same apartment block as her but despite her pleas he is acquitted. When he then goes on to rape her younger sister, she takes the law into her own hands.

      a. Lipstick
      b. Jackson County Jail
      c. The Star Chamber

104 An American mathematician and his wife return to the village in England where she was born and he is taunted by the locals, the ill-feeling finally building to a siege of their cottage and horrific violence.

    a. Death Weekend

    b. Straw Dogs

    c. Blind Terror

105 A band of particularly savage Apache braves break out of a reservation and are pursued by a detachment of cavalry led by an idealistic young lieutenant who is guided by a seasoned tracker and his Indian companion.

    a. The Searchers

    b. Major Dundee

    c. Ulzana's Raid

106 Two identical twins share everything including women, but when one of them falls in love with a patient at their clinic he finds that his love drives him to drug addition, despair and then madness.

    a. Twins

    b. Dead Ringers

    c. Basket Case

107 A widower and a young woman viewing an apartment fall into a relationship based solely on sex, a soulless union made all the more bitter by the man's hatred of his dead wife but his hatred of women turns to love when *he* falls for the young woman but finds that *she* has tired of him.

    a. The Passenger

    b. Henry and June

    c. Last Tango in Paris

108 Two peace-loving bikers decide to ride across America and, in the process, they come across drug addicts, crooked lawyers and, most horrifically of all, the violent antithesis of all they hold dear in the shape of two gun-toting lorry drivers.

        a. Easy Rider
        b. Breaking Point
        c. Dirty Mary, Crazy Larry

109 In the dying days of the Old West a gang of outlaws realize that they have outlived their time and plan to pull off one final job, which they do for a Mexican general. This leads them to their inevitable, and wished-for, violent deaths.
        a. The Professionals
        b. The Wild Bunch
        c. The Revengers

110 Four men hijack a New York subway train, taking some passengers prisoner, they then demand a ransom, threatening to kill one hostage for every minute the money is overdue. A detective tries to free the captured hostages.
        a. Ransom
        b. Subway
        c. The Taking of Pelham 123

111 A Mexican landowner, whose daughter has been made pregnant, offers a huge bounty for the head of anyone who can find her violator. (No clues needed here, I wouldn't have thought. Have a guess ...)

112 A murderer hides out in a girls' college, murdering those inside one by one, baffling the police who cannot work out how he can get away every time so quickly. The answer finally comes via the phone.
        a. Silent Night, Bloody Night
        b. When a Stranger Calls
        c. Black Christmas

113 A member of an off-shoot of the CIA is shot and crippled by a man he thought was his friend. He overcomes pain and disability to hunt the man down after discovering he's a double agent.

      a. The Russia House
      b. The Killer Elite
      c. The Internecine Project

114 A gang of Hell's Angels discover the secret of life after death but, in order to return and retain everlasting life, they first have to commit suicide.

      a. The Wild One
      b. Hell on Wheels
      c. Psychomania

115 An architect is horrified when his wife and daughter are attacked by muggers. Realizing that the police are powerless to help him, he takes the law into his own hands. (You shouldn't need any help here, either ...)

116 An idealistic motorcycle cop with dreams of becoming a detective finally gets his wish but discovers that treachery and double-dealing goes on and, when he tries to fight against it he is forced back onto the roads where, ultimately, he meets a very violent death.

      a. The Road Warrior
      b. Electra Glide in Blue
      c. The Detective

117 A branch of the CIA, especially employed to read books and find out if any real-life CIA activity is being duplicated, are wiped out by gunmen when they accidentally stumble on a plan which the top brass want to keep quiet. The sole survivor of the massacre tries to find out what or who is behind the slaughter.

a. Three Days of the Condor
b. The Parallax View
c. All the President's Men

118 Three Vietnam veterans, indoctrinated with killing, periodically kidnap a couple of people then release them into a specially constructed area and hunt them to the death.

a. The Most Dangerous Game
b. Open Season
c. Short Time

119 A maverick cop is forced to battle both his superiors and the Mafia as he fights to uncover a conspiracy which will lead to the assassination of several top gang bosses.

a. Dirty Harry
b. Ten to Midnight
c. The Stone Killer

120 A blind girl is menaced by drug pushers who know that she has heroin hidden in her apartment.

a. Wait Until Dark
b. Blind Terror
c. Blind Fury

121 A detective is faced with murders committed by a killer who has apparently been dead for 13 years. The answer lies in satanism and possession.

a. The Exorcist Ii
b. House of Exorcism
c. The Exorcist III

122 A woman is raped by a dwarf and gives birth to a monstrously deformed baby which is also possessed by the Devil.

> a. The Devil Within Her
> b. I Don't Want to be Born
> c. Three Men and a Baby

123 A jewel thief decides to work for an organization but finds that they try to control not only the way he works but also the way he lives, leading to a violent climax.

> a. Thief
> b. Violent Streets
> c. The Jericho Mile

124 A young man, in the process of delivering a car, picks up a murderous hitch-hiker and finds his life and the lives of all those he comes into contact with threatened by the homicidal stranger. (You're on your own again . . .)

125 In a dingy flat in Earl's Court a beautiful Belgian manicurist slowly goes insane, finally killing two people as she descends ever deeper into madness.

> a. The Tenant
> b. The Lodger
> c. Repulsion

126 A husband-and-wife bank robbery team pull one final job but have to fight their way to Mexico pursued by one of their gang, the police *and* the brothers of the man who hired them to do the robbery in the first place who the wife later kills. The final shoot-out takes place in a seedy El Paso hotel.

a. The Getaway
b. Trackdown
c. Eight Million Ways to Die

127 A policeman, on the trail of a child rapist, is finally forced, by the rapist himself, to admit to having similarly dark feelings. The admission of which causes him to snap and kill the rapist.

        a. Presumed Innocent
        b. The Offence
        c. Revenge

128 A Great White shark ... (I'm leaving it at that)

129 Marlon Brando plays the part of a Mafia Don ...

130 A young girl, possessed by the Devil ... (Yes, I know we've already had this one)

Odds And Ends

When I first agreed to do this book I suggested that it should contain 1000 questions. Well, what a comedian ... I can't even say that I decided on 1000 questions because I was pissed at the time (I don't drink any more; well, not since trying to take my trousers off over my head one night many moons ago ...). A thousand just seemed like a nice round number. Number it is, round it is (whatever the hell that means) but NICE it most certainly is not. Not when you're staring at a blank sheet of paper, your mind acting like an epileptic roladex flying back and forth over the thousands of films you've seen, trying to pick out, first, a suitable film, and then a suitable question.

The reason for this last batch of ranting, by the way, is that if you've battled your way through every single question so far you may have discovered that you have answered 35 short of that magical and yet tortuous figure of 1000. So, this next section is made up of just 35 questions to reach that milestone and the only reason you're faced with these remaining questions is because yours truly, who, when asked to do this book, decided to open his mouth before putting his brain in gear, is determined to reach that milestone with you.

So, for the last time, with the most motley assortment

of questions possible, you score one point for a correct answer.

For those of you who haven't bothered to battle your way through every question and, instead, have just dipped into the book, I DON'T BLAME YOU . . .

Those of you who have battled through right from the beginning of Section One, I admire and respect your stamina, I thank you for your interest and I hope that they put both you *and* I in a comfortable padded cell . . .

1 At the end of VILLAGE OF THE DAMNED, the hero tried to blow up the alien children with a bomb but, because he knew they could read his thoughts he concentrated his mind on another object. What was that other object?

> a. An iceberg
> b. A stone wall
> c. A skyscraper

2 Roger Corman made many films in the sixties based on Edgar Allan Poe stories. One of these films was attributed to Poe but its only connection with him was by way of a poem he'd written. What was the film?

> a. Murders in the Rue Morgue
> b. The Premature Burial
> c. The Haunted Palace

3 Which brilliant horror writer was actually responsible for the source material of the film in the question above?

> a. Robert E. Howard
> b. H.P. Lovecraft
> c. Algernon Blackwood

4 Sticking with H.P. Lovecraft for a moment, a film was made in 1968 based on one of his stories and starring Boris Karloff. What was the film called?

> a. Scream and Scream Again
> b. Night of the Comet
> c. Die, Monster, Die

5 Roger Corman's early career was littered with 'B' movies many of which he shot in an incredibly short time. Which film took just three days to shoot?

a. Little Shop of Horrors
b. The Terror
c. The Fall of the House of Usher

6 In MASQUE OF THE RED DEATH, what disguise does Patrick Magee wear for the actual dance?

a. A chicken costume
b. A gorilla costume
c. A priest's costume

7 In the same film, Hazel Court comes to a particularly nasty end because of her own pet. What is it?

a. A dog
b. A panther
c. A falcon

8 TALES OF TERROR was a compendium of three stories all based on Edgar Allan Poe works. 'The Black Cat' was one; 'The Facts of the Case of M. Valdemar' was another. What was the third?

a. The Cask of Amontillado
b. The Tell-Tale Heart
c. Morella

9 In THE HAUNTED PALACE, Vincent Price portrayed a reincarnated warlock who sought vengeance against the descendants of those who had burned him alive hundreds of years earlier. How did he dispose of Elisha Cook?

a. Stabbed him with a red hot sword
b. Poured petrol on him and set fire to him
c. Flayed him alive then cremated him

10 In THE TOMB OF LIGEIA, what kind of creature acts as a 'familiar' for the ghostly presence of Vincent Price's first wife?

a. A dog
b. A bat
c. A cat

11 What kind of creature was featured in THE BLOOD BEAST TERROR?

a. A giant raven
b. A giant moth
c. A giant bat

12 Compendium horror movies, featuring three, four or sometimes five short stories within the framework of one film have proved successful, so the following few questions concern these 'collections' of stories. The first one concerns TWICE TOLD TALES and a character played by Vincent Price in the first of the three stories. The elixir invented by Dr Heidegger gave him what?

a. Immortality
b. His lost youth
c. Invincibility

13 What was the setting which linked the five stories in DR TERROR'S HOUSE OF HORRORS?

a. A plane
b. A coach
c. A train

14 In the same film, Christopher Lee played an art critic who is pursued by what?

a. The ghost of the man who he's run down
b. The poltergeist
c. A severed hand

15 In TORTURE GARDEN, Burgess Meredith offered to show five people a glimpse of their futures. What was the name of the character he played?

     a. Dr Diablo
     b. Dr Death
     c. Dr Destiny

16 In the same film, Michael Bryant sees that his future involves a rather nasty encounter with a cat that eats a particular part of the human anatomy. Which part?

     a. The head
     b. The brain
     c. The eyes

17 In THE HOUSE THAT DRIPPED BLOOD, Jon Pertwee finds that by wearing one particular piece of clothing he is transformed into a vampire. Which item of clothing?

     a. A tie pin shaped like a bat
     b. A cloak
     c. A top hat rumoured to have belonged to a vampire

18 Who played the Crypt Keeper in TALES FROM THE CRYPT?

     a. Sir John Mills
     b. Sir Alec Guiness
     c. Sir Ralph Richardson

19 In the same film, Nigel Patrick plays the sadistic head of an institute for the blind who finally comes to a terrible end. He is given the choice of either squeezing down a very narrow corridor lined with razor blades or what?

a. Facing his own ravenously hungry dog
b. Being blindfolded and forced to fight a
   blind man with a razor
c. Being blinded by two needles through his
   eyes

20 Who played the part of the new psychiatrist coming
to take over the ASYLUM?

a. Peter Davidson
b. Robert Powell
c. Robin Nedwell

21 In the same film, Patrick Magee created and
controlled a particular type of creature. What was it?

a. A murderous mannequin
b. A clay man
c. A robot

22 VAULT OF HORROR featured an episode where the
maniacally neat Terry Thomas is finally killed by his wife
who then bottles his body parts and neatly labels them.
What does she put in the jar marked 'Odds and Ends'?

a. His eyes
b. His genitals
c. His moustache and eyebrows

23 The same film features an episode concerning
vampires during which Daniel Massey finds himself in a
particular venue run by the night dwellers. What kind of
place is it?

a. A cinema
b. A blood bank
c. A restaurant

24 What setting links the four tales in FROM BEYOND THE GRAVE?

      a. An antique shop
      b. A library
      c. A hairdresser's

25 In THE MONSTER CLUB, John Carradine was introduced to the various members of the club by Vincent Price, one of whom was the offspring of a human and a ghoul. What was this creature called?

      a. A ghouman
      b. A humgoo
      c. A houl

26 CREEPSHOW featured five stories by Stephen King. The last of them, 'They're Creeping Up on You' had E.G. Marshall attacked and eaten by what kind of creature?

      a. Rats
      b. Frogs
      c. Cockroaches

27 CREEPSHOW 2 featured one episode with some teenagers menaced while on an excursion to a lake. What kind of vessel were they using on the water?

      a. A canoe
      b. A raft
      c. A dinghy

28 In TALES THAT WITNESS MADNESS, who played the part of the psychiatrist showing Jack Hawkins around the asylum?

      a. Donald Pleasence
      b. Donald Sinden
      c. Geoffrey Bayldon

29 The Italian cinema has produced some truly awful horror films over the years (apart from some of Dario Argento's films) and they seem chiefly concerned with a never-ending procession of moronic zombie films. The next few questions concern those pictures where, most of the time, you're left wondering whether or not the pictures were written and directed by someone with advanced brain death too ... Among the many repulsive scenes in CITY OF THE LIVING DEAD, there is one in which a girl vomits. But no, folks, this is not your usual diced carrot job; she vomits up what?

    a. Maggots
    b. Her own intestines
    c. Someone else's intestines

30 What kind of building do the zombies in THE BEYOND inhabit?

    a. A church
    b. A hotel
    c. A castle

31 What is the name of the doctor in THE HOUSE BY THE CEMETERY who experiments with corpses?

    a. Dr Stein
    b. Dr Feinstein
    c. Dr Freudstein

32 In the un-cut version of ZOMBIE FLESH EATERS, a woman has her eye pierced by what?

    a. A knitting needle
    b. A razor-sharp shard of glass
    c. A long splinter of wood

33 Right, to finish off with some Urban Horror stuff and, for these last three, you can figure them out yourself. No multiple choice . . .

Which real-life comedian's life and death were depicted in the film WIRED?

34 In HALLOWEEN, which film was on the TV being watched by Jamie Lee Curtis and the two children she'd been left to look after? (I *will* give you a clue though. It was a film which the director of Halloween, John Carpenter, would later go on to remake himself in 1982.)

35 The best horror contains humour so this final question is concerned with the best horror spoof ever made, YOUNG FRANKENSTEIN. In a beautifully accurate scene, the monster (played by Peter Boyle) stumbles upon a blind beggar (echoing the scene in BRIDE OF FRANKENSTEIN) who first dumps hot soup in his lap, smashes the cup he intends to drink from, then lights his thumb while trying to show him how to smoke a cigar. A very big star played the part of the blind man but didn't appear in the credits. Who was he?

Right, that's your lot. One thousand questions. I hope you did all right; the answers are coming up for you to check. However you did, I hope you enjoyed yourself. If you went for all 1000 then I reckon you deserve to do what I'm now off to do: nip off down the pub.

If you see me in there, buy me a Perrier water.

Take care of yourselves and see you around

Shaun Hutson

The Answers...

The Silents

1b, 2c, 3b, 4b, 5c, 6b, 7a, 8b, 9b, 10c, 11b, 12a, 13c, 14b, 15c, 16a, 17b, 18b, 19c, 20b, 21c, 22b, 23b, 24a, 25c.

The Golden (and not quite so golden) Age of Horror Films 1930–1956

1b, 2c, 3b, 4c, 5b, 6c, 7b, 8a, 9b, 10c, 11c, 12a, 13c, 14b, 15a, 16b, 17c, 18b, 19c, 20a, 21b, 22b, 23c, 24b, 25c, 26a, or b or even c believe it or not because Mae Clarke had been Frankenstein's bride in FRANKENSTEIN, Valerie Hobson was his bride in BRIDE OF FRANKENSTEIN but Elsa Lanchester played the monster's mate so, all three are right if you like, 27b, 28a, 29c, 30b, 31c, 32b, 33a, 34c, 35a, 36b, 37c, 38a, 39b, 40b, 41a, 42 True, 43b, 44c, 45a, 46b, 47c, 48a, 49c, 50b, 51c, 52b, 53a, 54b, and d, 55a, 56b, 57c, 58b, 59c, 60b, 61c, 62a, 63b, 64c, 65b, 66c, 67c, 68c, 69c, 70b, 71c, 72b, 73c, 74c, 75b, 76b, 77c, 78b, 79a, 80b and e, 81b – You can't see 3-D with only one eye – Try it. 82c, 83b, 84c, 85b, 86b, 87b, 88b, 89c, 90a, 91c, 92b, 93a, 94b, 95b, 96c, 97b, 98c, 99a, and b – The fly with the human head was eaten by a spider and the human with the fly head was crushed in a hydraulic press. 100b and c.

'Quote, Unquote' (Part 1)

1b, 2b, 3c, 4b, 5a, 6c, 7b, 8b, 9c, 10c, 11a, 12c, 13b, 14c, 15b, 16c, 17b, 18a, 19a, 20a, 21b, 22c, 23b, 24c, 25b, 26a, 27b, 28c, 29b, 30c.

Hammer Films

1c, 2b, 3a, 4b, 5c, 6c, 7c, 8c, 9b, 10a, 11b, 12c, 13b, 14c, 15b, 16a, 17b, 18c, 19a, 20b, 21a, 22c, 23b, 24c, 25c, 26b, 27c, 28b, 29a, 30c, 31c, 32a, 33b, 34a, 35c, 36a, 37c, 38b, 39a, 40b, 41b, 42c, 43a, 44b, 45c, 46b, 47c, 48c, 49b, 50a, 51b, 52b, 53c, 54c, 55b, 56b, 57c, 58a, 59a, 60b, 61c, 62b, 63c, 64b, 65a, 66c, 67b, 68a, 69b, 70c, 71b, 72c, 73a, 74b, 75c, 76 True, 77c, 78b, 79c, 80c, 81c, 82b, 83a, 84c, 85c.

'Quote, Unquote' (Part 2)

1a, 2c, 3b, 4c, 5b, 6c, 7b, 8c, 9b, 10c, 11b, 12c, 13b, 14a, 15b.

Urban Horror

1b, 2c, 3a, 4b, 5c, 6b, 7b, 8c, 9b, 10a, 11b, 12c, 13 Michael
Corleone played by Al Pacino, Sonny Corleone played by
James Caan, Fredo Corleone played by John Cazale and
Connie Corleone played by Talia Shire, 14b, 15c, 16a, 17b, 18c,
19b, 20c, 21b, 22c, 23a, 24b, 25b, 26c, 27a, 28b, 29c, 30a,
31b, 32a, 33b, 34 The Towering Inferno, 35b, 36c, 37b, 38c,
39b, 40a, 41a, 42b, 43b, 44a, 45b, 46c, 47b, 48a, 49b, 50a,
51c, 52b, 53b, 54c, 55a, 56b, 57a, 58b, 59c, 60a, 61b, 62c,
63a, 64b, 65c, 66b, 67b, 68a, 69b, 70c, 71a, 72b, 73c, 74c,
75a, 76b, 77a, 78b, 79b, 80b, 81c, 82c, 83b, 84c, 85c, 86c,
87a, 88b, 89c, 90a, 91b, 92c, 93b and f, 94b, 95c, 96 John
Rambo, 97b, 98a, 99c, e, f and h, 100c, 101b, 102c, 103c,
104b, 105a, 106a, 107c, 108a, 109b, 110a, 111b, 112b, 113a,
114b, 115c, 116c, 117c, 118b, 119c, 120b, 121a, 122c, 123a,
124b, 125c, 126a, 127c, 128b, 129b, 130b, 131a, 132b, 133b,
134c, 135b, 136c, 137a, 138b, 139c, 140b, 141c, 142b, 143b,
144c, 145b, 146a and b, 147c, 148b, 149c, 150b, 151a, 152b,
153a, 154c, 155b, 156a, 157c, 158a, 159c, 160a, 161 Tom Bell
who played Jack MacVitie and Steven Berkoff who played
George Cornell, 162b, 163b, 164b, 165c, 166b, 167c, 168b,
169b, 170a, 171c, 172b, 173c, 174b, 175b, 176c, 177b, 178c,
179a, 180b, 181c, 182a, 183b, 184a, 185c, 186b, 187a, 188b,
189c, 190a, 191b, 192 Diane Keaton and Talia Shire, 193c,
194b, 195a, 196b, 197c, 198a, 199c, 200a.

'Quote, Unquote' (Part 3)

1 Sylvester Stallone to Brian Dennehy in FIRST BLOOD
2 Robert Blake to an unnamed girl in ELECTRA GLIDE IN
   BLUE
3 Clint Eastwood to John Vernon in DIRTY HARRY
4 Warren Oates to unnamed woman in DILLINGER
5 Angela Lansbury to Sarah Patterson in THE COMPANY OF
   WOLVES

6 Robert Duvall to Martin Sheen in APOCALYPSE NOW
7 Dick O'Neill to Walter Matthau in THE TAKING OF PELHAM 123
8 Eric Bogosian to his listeners in TALK RADIO
9 Marlon Brando to Robert Duvall in THE GODFATHER
10 Warren Oates to Emilio Fernandez in BRING ME THE HEAD OF ALFREDO GARCIA
11 William Holden to Ben Johnson in THE WILD BUNCH
12 John Houseman to James Caan in ROLLERBALL
13 Burt Lancaster to Bruce Davidson in ULZANA'S RAID
14 James Keach to an unnamed Pinkerton agent in THE LONG RIDERS
15 Hal Holbrook to Michael Douglas in THE STAR CHAMBER
16 Al Pacino to Charles Durning in DOG DAY AFTERNOON
17 Robert De Niro in RAGING BULL
18 David Warner to James Mason in CROSS OF IRON
19 Gene Hackman to Brad Dourif in MISSISSIPPI BURNING
20 Robert Ryan to Albert Dekker in THE WILD BUNCH
21 Eddie Murphy to Nick Nolte in ANOTHER 48 HOURS
22 Steven Seagal in MARKED FOR DEATH
23 Jason Miller to Ellen Burstyn in THE EXORCIST
24 William Peterson in MANHUNTER
25 Talia Shire to Andy Garcia in THE GODFATHER III
26 Robert De Niro in TAXI DRIVER
27 Desk sergeant to Al Pacino in SERPICO
28 Anthony Zerbe to Charlton Heston in THE OMEGA MAN
29 Peter Fonda to Richard Lynch in OPEN SEASON
30 Vincent Gardenia in DEATH WISH
31 Al Lettieri to Steve McQueen in THE GETAWAY
32 Nicol Williamson in THE WILBY CONSPIRACY
33 Gene Hackman to Harris Yulin in NIGHT MOVES
34 Burt Young to James Caan in THE KILLER ELITE
35 Lee Marvin to Richard Burton in THE KLANSMAN
36 James Coburn to Larry Wilcox in THE LAST HARD MEN
37 Bruce Willis screaming into a radio in DIE HARD
38 Robert Shaw to his captives in THE TAKING OF PELHAM123
39 Sean Connery to Kevin Costner in THE UNTOUCHABLES
40 Michael Douglas to Andy Garcia in BLACK RAIN
41 Gary Kemp to Martin Kemp in THE KRAYS

42 Jason Robards to Robert Redford in ALL THE PRESIDENT'S MEN
43 Clint Eastwood in SUDDEN IMPACT
44 Ray Liotta in GOODFELLAS
45 Clint Eastwood to Andy Robinson in DIRTY HARRY
46 Robert Prosky in CHRISTINE
47 James Remar in 48 HOURS
48 Jamie Lee Curtis in BLUE STEEL
49 Martin Sheen in APOCALYPSE NOW
50 James Woods in COP

Everything But The Kitchen Sink ...

1c, 2c, 3b, 4b, 5c, 6a, 7b, 8c, 9a, 10b, 11c, 12b, 13c, 14c, 15a, 16a, 17c, 18b, 19c, 20b, 21c, 22c, 23b, 24 Alfred Hitchcock, 25b, 26c, 27a, 28b, 29c, 30a, 31c, 32b, 33a, 34b, 35b, 36c, 37c, 38c, 39b, 40c, 41a, 42b, 43c, 44c, 45b, 46c, 47b, 48a, 49b, 50c, 51c, 52b, 53b, 54c, 55b, 56c, 57c, 58b, 59b, 60a, 61c, 62c, 63a, 64c, 65b, 66b, 67c, 68b, 69a, 70 666, 71b, 72a, 73b, 74b, 75c, 76a, 77c, 78b, 79c, 80b, 81a, 82b, 83c, 84b, 85c, 86a, 87b, 88b, 89c, 90c, 91b, 92b, 93a, 94c, 95a, 96c, 97b, 98c, 99b, 100a, 101b, 102c, 103b, 104c, 105c, 106a, 107b, 108c, 109c, 110b, 111c, 112b, 113b, 114c, 115a, 116b, 117b, 118c, 119c, 120a, 121c, 122c, 123b, 124a, 125 Arnold Schwarzenegger, 126c, 127a, 128b, 129c, 130b, 131a, 132b, 133b, 134c, 135a, 136b, 137c, 138b, 139a, 140b, 141c, 142c, 143b, 144c, 145a, 146b, 147c, 148c, 149c, 150b, 151c, 152c, 153c, 154b, 155c, 156a, 157c, 158b, 159a, 160c, 161c, 162b, 163c, 164b, 165c, 166b, 167b, 168b, 169c, 170 Alien, 171 False, but, you never know ... 172b, 173b, 174c, 175c, 176b, 177a, 178b, 179c, 180b, 181c, 182a, 183b, 184c, 185a, 186b, 187a, 188c, 189b, 190c, 191a, 192b, 193c, 194b, 195a, 196c, 197b, 198c, 199c, 200b.

Cast Off

1b, 2c, 3b, 4c, 5a, 6b, 7c, 8a, 9c, 10b, 11b, 12a, 13c, 14a, 15b, 16a, 17c, 18b, 19b, 20c, 21b, 22a, 23b, 24a, 25a, 26b, 27c, 28b, 29b, 30b, 31a, 32c, 33c, 34a, 35c, 36b, 37c, 38b, 39c,

40b, 41a, 42. The Exorcist, 43b, 44c, 45a, 46b, 47 You could have either a or b because in Halloween and Halloween 2 Dick Warlock played Michael Myers and also, in Halloween 2 Nancy Loomis appeared briefly as a corpse. 48c, 49a, 50b, 51b, 52c, 53 Jaws, 54a, 55b, 56c, 57b, 58c, 59c, 60b, 61a, 62b, 63c, 64c, 65c, 66a, 67b, 68b, 69c, 70a, 71a, 72c, 73a, 74c, 75c, 76a, 77c, 78b, 79c, 80b, 81c, 82b, 83a, 84b, 85 Apocalypse Now, 86b, 87c, 88b, 89c, 90c, 91b, 92b, 93c, 94b, 95b, 96c, 97a, 98b, 99b, 100c.

In With A Shout

1a, 2b, 3a, 4c, 5c, 6b, 7b, 8a, 9b, 10a, 11c, 12b, 13c, 14b, 15b, 16a, 17b, 18c, 19b, 20c, 21a, 22b, 23a, 24b, 25c, 26b, 27c, 28b, 29c, 30b.

Once Upon A Time ...

1b, 2c, 3b, 4c, 5b, 6a, 7c, 8b, 9c, 10b, 11c, 12c, 13a, 14b, 15c, 16a, 17c, 18a, 19c, 20b, 21c, 22b, 23c, 24a, 25b, 26c, 27b, 28a, 29b, 30b, 31a, 32c, 33b, 34c, 35b, 36b, 37b, 38c, 39b, 40 The Omen, 41b, 42c, 43a, 44b, 45a, 46c, 47c, 48 Rosemary's Baby, 49b, 50c, 51b, 52 The Thing, 53b, 54c, 55c, 56c, 57a, 58b, 59c, 60c, 61b, 62a, 63b, 64c, 65b, 66c, 67c, 68a, 69b, 70c, 71a, 72b, 73b, 74c, 75b, 76b, 77c, 78b, 79c, 80 Fatal Attraction, 81b, 82c, 83b, 84b, 85c, 86b, 87c, 88b, 89c, 90a, 91c, 92c, 93a, 94c, 95a, 96 Midnight Express, 97b, 98c, 99a, 100 Taxi Driver, 101b, 102a, 103a, 104b, 105c, 106b, 107c, 108a, 109b, 110c, 111 Bring Me the Head of Alfredo Garcia, 112c, 113b, 114c, 115 Death Wish, 116b, 117a, 118b, 119c, 120a, 121c, 122b, 123 a, or b – This film was known in America as Thief and in Europe as Violent Streets 124 The Hitcher, 125c, 126a, 127b, 128 Jaws, 129 The Godfather, 130 The Exorcist.

Odds And Ends

1b, 2c, 3b, 4c, 5b, 6b, 7c, 8c, 9b, 10c, 11b, 12b, 13c, 14c, 15a, 16a, 17b, 18c, 19a, 20b, 21a, 22b, 23c, 24a, 25b, 26c, 27b, 28a, 29b, 30b, 31c, 32c, 33 John Belushi, 34 The Thing, 35 Gene Hackman.